The Heineman Science Scheme

Book 1

Foundation Edition

Byron Dawson

Heinemann

Heinemann Educational Publishers
Halley Court, Jordan Hill, Oxford, OX2 8EJ
Part of Harcourt Education Limited

Heinemann is the registered trademark of
Harcourt Education Limited

© Harcourt Education Limited 2002

First published 2002

07 06 05 04
10 9 8 7 6 5 4 3 2

British Library Cataloguing in Publication Data is available
from the British Library on request.

ISBN 0 435 58330 1

Edited by Ruth Holmes and Mick Watson

Typeset by Techset Ltd, Gateshead

Original illustrations © Harcourt Education Limited 2002

Illustrated by Hardlines

Printed and bound in Italy by Printer Trento S.r.l.

Cover photo: © Stone/Christophe Burki

Picture research by Thelma Gilbert

Index by Ann Hall

Acknowledgements
Every effort has been made to contact copyright holders of
material reproduced in this book. Any omissions will be
rectified in subsequent printings if notice is given to the
publishers.

The author and publishers would like to thank the following
for permission to use photographs:

T = top *B* = bottom *R* = right *L* = left *M* = middle

SPL = Science Photo Library   OSF = Oxford Scientific Films

3 SPL; 5 Biophoto Associates; 6 both Biophoto Associates; 8
TL SPL/John Walsh, TR SPL/Andrew Leonard, TM SPL/BSIP
VEM; 10 SPL/Astrid & Hans Frieder Michler; 12 TL OSF; TR
Harry Smith; 14 OSF; 15 T Roger Scruton, M OSF; 22
Bubbles; 25 SPL/Peter Ryan; 28 T Photodisc, M and B OSF;
29 OSF; 31 TL and TR OSF, B Andrew Lambert; 32 T and M
Natural Visions, B OSF; 33 both OSF; 34 TL Still Pictures, TR
Photodisc, ML OSF, MR Bruce Coleman, BR OSF; 35 both
OSF; 39 T Game Conservancy Trust/John Darling, M and B
OSF; 40 T OSF, M Bruce Coleman, B Stone/Bon Thomas; 43
both OSF; 48 T and M Roger Scruton, B Bruce Coleman/
Scott Neilsen; 52 both Roger Scruton; 54 and 55 all Andrew
Lambert; 56 Philip Parkhouse; 57 both Andrew Lambert; 58
T and M Roger Scruton, B SPL/Adam Hart Davis; 59
Environmental Images; 60 Roger Scruton; 62 TL OSF, TR
Roger Scruton; 63 T Roger Scruton, ML and MR Andrew
Lambert; 64 T Roger Scruton, B Andrew Lambert; 65 all
Andrew Lambert; 67 TL and TR Roger Scruton; TM OSF, B
Andrew Lambert; 68 T Roger Scruton, B Byron Dawson; 69
Andrew Lambert; 70 TL and TLM Roger Scruton, TRM and
TR Robert Harding; M Spectrum; 72 both Andrew Lambert;
74 T Bridgeman Art Library/Vatican Museums & Galleries,
BL Roger Scruton, BM Photodisc, BR Andrew Lambert; 75
TL and TM OSF, TR Robert Harding, BL Bruce Coleman,
BM and BR Roger Scruton; 76 all Andrew Lambert; 78 both
and 79 Roger Scruton; 80 T GSF, M Andrew Lambert, B OSF;
82 T Trevor Clifford, B Andrew Lambert; 83 both Andrew
Lambert; 84 T Andrew Lambert, B Robert Harding/ Brigitte
Bott; 85 both Andrew Lambert; 86 T Salt Union, M OSF, B
Roger Scruton; 87 all Andrew Lambert; 88 Gareth Boden; 89
SPL/Dr. Jeremy Burgess; 90 TL and TR Roger Scruton, B
Andrew Lambert; 91 and 92 all Andrew Lambert; 93 Ian
Bradley; 94 and 95 both Andrew Lambert; 96T Colorsport, M
Corbis/Robert Estall, B Photodisc; 97 Photodisc; 98 Andrew
Lambert; 99 Roger Scruton; 100 T Roger Scruton, M
Environmental Images, B OSF; 101 Corbis/Robert Estall; 102
all Photodisc; 103 T SPL/Martin Bond, M OSF; 104 T
Bubbles, M SPL/John Heseltine, B Andrew Lambert; 105 and
106 all Photodisc; 108 and 109 all Andrew Lambert; 110 Peter
Gale; 112 Andrew Lambert; 114 T Andrew Lambert, M Roger
Scruton; 119 SPL; 120 both, 121 both, 122 all and 123
Andrew Lambert; 124 T Corbis/Lester Lefkowitz, M
Spectrum, B Spectrum; 126 T Colorsport, B Roger Scruton;
127 TL Robert Harding, TM, TR and B Photodisc; 128 Peter
Morris; 131 Andrew Lambert; 132 both and 136 Photodisc;
137 SPL/Dan Schechter; 140 SPL/Eckhard Slawik; 143 all
Photodisc; 144 T and B Photodisc, M SPL; 145 Photodisc.

Tel: 01865 888058 email: info.he@heinemann.co.uk

Welcome to Heinemann Science Scheme!

This is the first Foundation book in a series of three. They will cover all the science you need to learn at Key Stage 3.

The book is divided into twelve units. Each unit has several topics. A topic is on two pages. In each topic you will find:

● **Questions as you go along like this:**

   ⓑ What is the solute in salt solution?

   These are quick questions to check that you understand things before you carry on.

● **Questions in a box at the end of the spread with this heading:**

   QUESTIONS

   These help you bring together everything in the topic.

● **A list of key points at the end with this heading:**

   KEY POINTS

   These summarise what you have studied in the topic.

Important words are highlighted in **bold**. They are all in a glossary at the back of the book with their meanings. You can look them up as you work through the book.

As you study Heinemann Science Scheme your teacher will give you activities and extra questions from the teacher's pack. There are also tests to help you and your teachers keep track of how you're doing.

We hope you enjoy studying science with Heinemann Science Scheme.

Contents

A Cells

WHAT ARE LIVING THINGS MADE FROM?

How do we know that something is alive?

All living plants and animals have some things in common.

Living things feed.

Plants make their own food. Animals feed on other plants or animals. This is called **nutrition**.

Living things move.

It is obvious that animals move about. But plants also move. They can turn their leaves to face the Sun.

Living things grow.

All living things start small and then grow bigger.

Living things reproduce.

All living things make new living things. Humans have babies and plants have seeds that grow into new plants.

What are organs?

Your body is made up of lots of **organs**. Each organ has a different job to do.

The picture shows some of the organs found in your body. Look at the picture carefully and answer these questions:

ⓐ Which organs in the body break down your food?

ⓑ Which organs in the body help you to move?

ⓒ Which organ pumps blood around your body?

ⓓ Which organ takes up oxygen from the air?

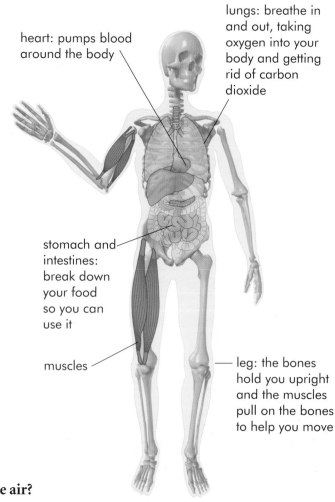

heart: pumps blood around the body

lungs: breathe in and out, taking oxygen into your body and getting rid of carbon dioxide

stomach and intestines: break down your food so you can use it

muscles

leg: the bones hold you upright and the muscles pull on the bones to help you move

Plant organs

Just like us, plants also have organs. The organs in plants do different jobs from the organs in humans.

Look at the picture and answer the following questions:

e Which organ makes food for the plant?

f Which organ is used for making new plants?

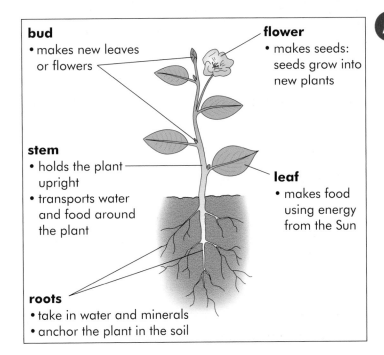

bud
• makes new leaves or flowers

flower
• makes seeds: seeds grow into new plants

stem
• holds the plant upright
• transports water and food around the plant

leaf
• makes food using energy from the Sun

roots
• take in water and minerals
• anchor the plant in the soil

What are organs made of?

Every organ in plants and animals is made up from **cells**. Cells are like tiny building blocks. They are so small that you cannot see them with your **naked eye**. To see them, you need to use a **microscope**.

The picture shows lots of the same kind of plant cells. A group of the same kind of cell is called a **tissue**. The picture shows tissue taken from an onion.

Organs are made from several different types of tissue.

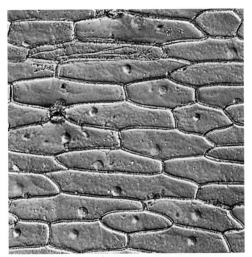

QUESTIONS

Copy these sentences and fill in the spaces using the words below:

cells   heart   organ   reproduce   tissue

Living things all feed, move, grow and _____ . Living things are made from small building blocks called _____ . A group of the same kind of cell is called a _____ . Groups of tissues make an _____ . An example of an organ is the _____ .

KEY POINTS

● All living things feed, move, grow and reproduce.

● Living things are made up of organs.

● Organs are made up of tissues.

● Tissues are made up of collections of the same kind of cell.

What are microscopes used for?

Microscopes are used for looking at very small things like cells. Microscopes make things look bigger. They magnify something so that we can see it.

Each part of the microscope does a different job.

Look at the picture of the microscope and answer the following questions.

ⓐ **Name the part that you look through.**

ⓑ **Name the part that reflects light into the microscope.**

ⓒ **Name the part where you place the thing you are going to look at.**

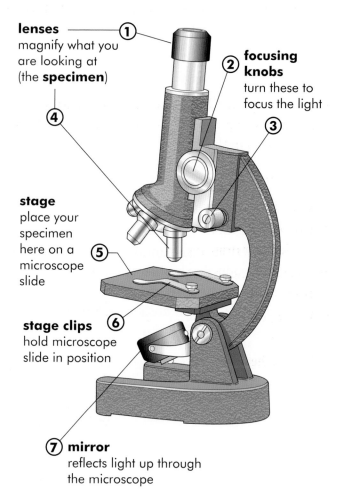

lenses
magnify what you are looking at (the **specimen**)

focusing knobs
turn these to focus the light

stage
place your specimen here on a microscope slide

stage clips
hold microscope slide in position

mirror
reflects light up through the microscope

What is magnification?

The microscope uses two lenses to make things look bigger. You look through one lens and the other one is just above the thing you are looking at. The number of times a microscope increases the size of an object is called the **magnification**.

How to use a microscope

1. Place a piece of onion tissue on a glass slide.

2. Add one drop of stain onto the onion tissue.

3. Place a glass **cover slip** onto the tissue.

The picture shows you how to lower the cover slip into place.

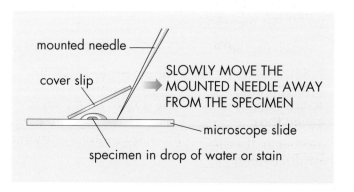

mounted needle

cover slip

SLOWLY MOVE THE MOUNTED NEEDLE AWAY FROM THE SPECIMEN

microscope slide

specimen in drop of water or stain

4. Place the slide onto the stage of the microscope.

5. Focus the microscope so that you can see the cells of the tissue.

ⓓ Sometimes you get bubbles of air trapped between the slide and the cover slip. This makes it difficult to see the cells under the microscope. Why should you try not to trap any bubbles of air?

How to draw what you see

Look at the photograph and drawing of part of a leaf. They show you how to make a good drawing of what you see through the microscope.

Here are some tips.

- Use a sharp pencil.
- Do not colour or shade your drawing.
- Your drawing should cover half a page.
- Do not draw it inside a circle.
- Write a heading.

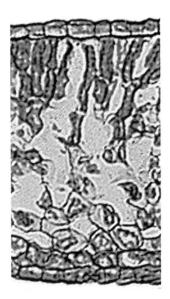
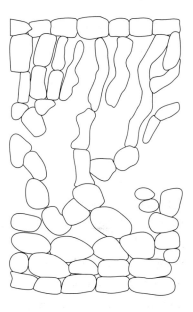

QUESTIONS

Copy these sentences and fill in the spaces using the words below:

bigger   lenses   magnification   mirror

Microscopes make things look _____ than they really are. The number of times a microscope increases the size of an object is called the _____ . Every microscope has two _____ . A _____ is used to reflect light into the microscope.

KEY POINTS

- Microscopes make things look bigger.

- Magnification is how much bigger something looks.

How cells were discovered

Before 1665, no one knew that living things were made of cells. It was only when English scientist Robert Hooke made the first simple microscope in 1665 that people saw cells for the first time.

Robert Hooke looked at tree bark under the microscope. He saw that it was made of lots of tiny boxes. He called these boxes 'cells'.

As more and more scientists began to use microscopes, they discovered that all living things were made of cells.

ⓐ **Why were cells not discovered before 1665?**

Scientists soon began to make much better microscopes. Today we have very powerful microscopes. They show us cells in much more detail.

The picture below shows cells seen under a very powerful microscope.

ⓑ **What differences can you see between the cells that Robert Hooke saw, and the cells seen using a modern powerful microscope?**

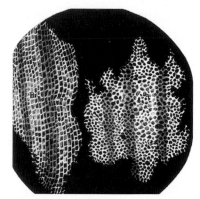

What Robert Hooke saw under his microscope

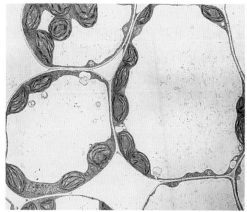

Plant cells seen using a powerful microscope

Animal and plant cells

Animal and plant cells look different from one another. This is because they do different jobs. Animal cells are like tiny bags. Plant cells are like tiny boxes.

Parts of the cell

Look at the pictures of an animal cell and a plant cell.

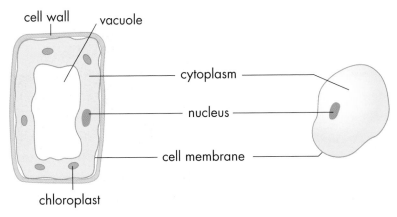

Plant cell   Animal cell

Things found in both animal and plant cells:

- The **nucleus**. This controls what happens in the cell.

- The **cytoplasm**. This is the cell's contents.

- The **cell membrane**. This holds the cell together.

Things found only in plant cells:

- The **cell wall**. This is like a box around the cell.
  It stops the cell changing shape.

- The **vacuole**. This is like a bubble of water that
  contains the cell sap.

- **Chloroplasts**. They catch light energy from the Sun.
  They use this energy to make food.

C Why can't animals make their own food?

KEY POINTS

- Scientists discovered cells by using a microscope.

- Animal and plant cells are different because they do different jobs.

- Different parts of the cell do different things.

QUESTIONS

Look at the following words. Make a list of all those that would only be found in a plant cell.

cell wall   cell membrane   chloroplast
cytoplasm   nucleus   vacuole

Cells are different

Look at the pictures of the cells. Even though they are all animal cells, they all look different.

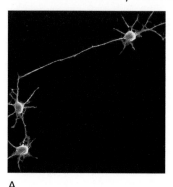

A

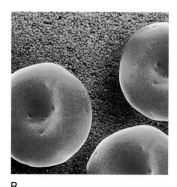

B

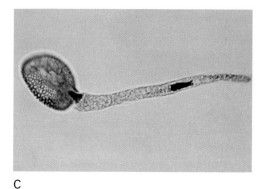

C

Why are cells different?

Cells are different because they do different jobs. Their different shapes help them to do their different jobs properly.

Red blood cells

Red blood cells carry oxygen around your body. They do not have a nucleus, so they have more room to carry oxygen.

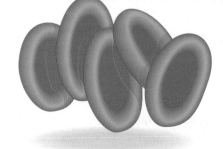

Sperm cells

Sperm cells are produced by male animals. A sperm cell joins with a female egg cell during reproduction. Sperm cells have long tails to help them swim so that they can find the female egg.

ⓐ **Which of the pictures at the top of the page do you think is a red blood cell?**

Egg cells

Egg cells are large so they can carry lots of food for the new baby.

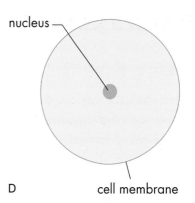

D   cell membrane

Nerve cells

Nerve cells are long. This is because they carry messages and instructions from one part of your body to another. They are rather like telephone wires.

ⓑ **Look at the two pictures D and E. Which one do you think is a nerve cell?**

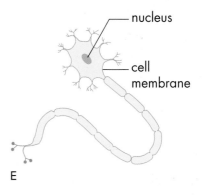

E

Root hair cells

Root hair cells are the tiny hairs that you can see on a plant's root. They have a very large surface area. This helps them absorb water and minerals from the soil.

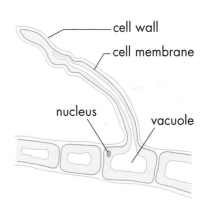

QUESTIONS

Copy these sentences and fill in the spaces using the words below:

red blood   sperm   egg   root hair   nerve

Plants absorb water from the soil through _____ cells. Animals send messages around their bodies along _____ cells. Some cells, like _____ cells, are large because they have a food store. _____ cells do not have a nucleus, so they can carry more oxygen. Some cells like _____ cells can move because they have a long tail.

KEY POINTS

- There are different types of cell.

- Cells are different because they do different jobs.

What is a tissue?

Cells that look the same and do the same job are often found together. These groups of cells are called **tissues**.

Muscle tissue is made from millions of muscle cells. One muscle cell on its own would not be much use. Millions of muscle cells working together can make us move.

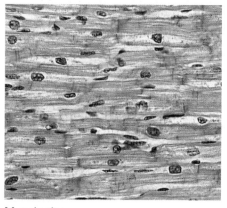

Muscle tissue

Plants also have tissue. Some cells in plants are like long tubes. They carry water up the plant from the roots. The tissue is called **xylem**.

ⓐ **What do we call lots of the same type of cell?**

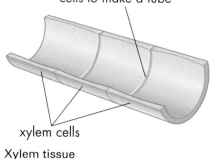

wall broken down between cells to make a tube

xylem cells

Xylem tissue

What is an organ?

An **organ** is made of several different types of tissue working together. Even though each tissue does a different job, they work together to make sure the organ can do its job.

A house is rather like an organ. Its job is to protect us and keep us warm and dry. The walls and roof are like a tissue. They keep out the cold and rain. Each brick in the wall, and tile in the roof, is like a single cell.

Water pipes in the house are like xylem tissue in plants. They provide different rooms with water.

ⓑ **Leaves have small holes to let in air. Which part of the house does this job?**

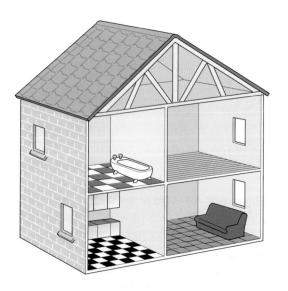

Look at the picture of the rabbit's leg.

The leg is an organ. It is made up of several different kinds of tissue.

c Which tissue helps the leg to move?

d Which tissue makes the leg stiff and rigid?

e Which tissue holds everything together?

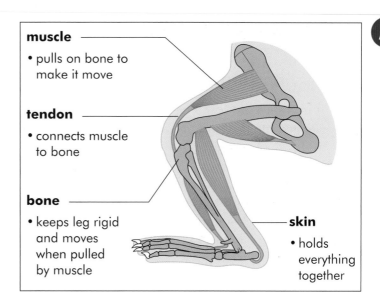

muscle
• pulls on bone to make it move

tendon
• connects muscle to bone

bone
• keeps leg rigid and moves when pulled by muscle

skin
• holds everything together

Look at the picture of the leaf. The leaf is an organ found in plants. Its job is to make food. To do this the leaf needs to catch sunlight. **Chloroplasts** catch sunlight. They are found inside most cells in the leaf.

The top layer of the leaf does not contain chloroplasts.

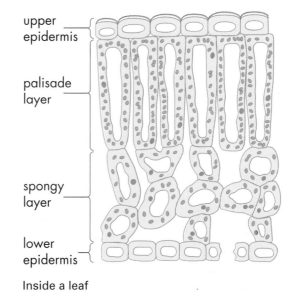

upper epidermis

palisade layer

spongy layer

lower epidermis

Inside a leaf

QUESTIONS

Copy this sentence and fill in the spaces using the words below:

organs   cells

Tissues are made of _____ , but _____ are made of tissues.

KEY POINTS

• A tissue is a group of similar cells doing the same job.

• An organ is a group of different tissues working together.

HOW ARE NEW CELLS MADE?

How living things grow

Most things start life very small.
They can grow to be very large.
Look at the picture of a young
redwood tree.

When fully grown this tree will be
one of the tallest trees in the world.
It gets this big because its cells divide
to make new cells. The tree grows
because it has more and more cells.

A young redwood   A fully-grown redwood

It starts with the nucleus

All cells divide in the same way.
The nucleus contains all the cell's
information. So first the nucleus
makes a copy of this information.
The nucleus then divides and each
new nucleus has one copy of the
information. The whole cell then
divides into two new ones. Look at
the picture below.

**ⓐ Why do you think the information in the nucleus
is copied?**

The two new small cells then grow until they reach
their normal size. The reason young children grow so
fast is because their cells are dividing very quickly.

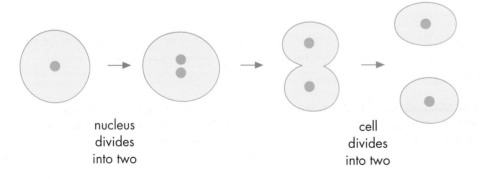

nucleus
divides
into two

cell
divides
into two

Making new organisms

Many living things reproduce when special cells from a male join with special cells from a female. This is called **fertilisation**. In plants, a male **pollen cell** joins with a female **egg cell**.

ⓑ **What is it called when a male cell joins with a female cell?**

How fertilisation happens in plants

Fertilisation happens inside flowers. Pollen cells are found inside pollen grains. Some pollen travels from one flower to another by wind. Some pollen is carried from one flower to another by insects.

When pollen arrives on the **stigma** of a new flower, this is called **pollination**.

The female egg cell is deep inside the flower. The pollen cannot get to the egg cell. Instead, it grows a tube that carries the pollen cell nucleus down to the **ovary**. Here the pollen cell nucleus joins with the egg cell.

This is called **fertilisation**. The fertilised cell divides, and grows to form a seed.

pollen grain containing pollen cell — stigma

pollen tube which grows out from pollen cell — style

nucleus of pollen cell moving down pollen tube

ovule containing egg cell — ovary

ⓒ **What is the difference between fertilisation and pollination?**

QUESTIONS

1 Draw a picture to show how a cell divides.

2 Look at the picture above about fertilisation in plants. Describe how the pollen cell nucleus reaches the ovary.

KEY POINTS

- Living things grow when cells divide.

- Cells divide by copying the information inside the nucleus.

- New organisms are made when a male cell fertilises a female cell.

B Reproduction

HOW DOES A NEW LIFE START?

Fertilisation

In the last unit we saw that plants and animals produce special cells for reproduction.

In animals the male cell is a **sperm cell**. The female cell is an **egg cell**. A sperm and egg cell join together to make the first cell of a new animal. This joining is called **fertilisation**.

ⓐ What is the male cell called?

ⓑ What is the female cell called?

Where fertilisation happens

Sometimes fertilisation happens outside the female's body. Female frogs release their eggs cells into the water. The male frogs then release their sperm over the top of the eggs to fertilise them. Because this happens outside the female frog's body, it is called **external fertilisation**.

Sometimes fertilisation happens inside the female's body. In land animals, the male's sperm is placed inside the female's body. The egg cell is fertilised inside the female. This is called **internal fertilisation**.

Caring for the offspring

Frogs

Once the eggs are fertilised, the male and female frogs have nothing more to do with them. They abandon the fertilised eggs. When the eggs hatch, the baby tadpoles have to look after themselves.

Because lots of the baby tadpoles will not survive, the parent frogs fertilise hundreds of eggs. This is to make sure that a few of them will survive and grow into frogs.

ⓒ Why do frogs lay so many eggs?

Humans

Humans produce much fewer children. Most parents have only two or three children. To make sure that the baby survives, the sperm from the father is placed inside the mother's body. Fertilisation is **internal**.

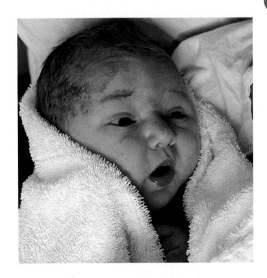

The growing baby spends nine months being protected and fed inside the mother's body. When the baby is born the parents will look after the baby for up to eighteen years.

d **Why do humans take so much care of their children?**

Other mammals

All mammals protect their offspring before birth by carrying them inside the mother's body. But when they are born, they will soon have to look after themselves.

This foal is ready to walk just a few minutes after it is born.

QUESTIONS

Copy these sentences and fill in the spaces using the words below:

fewer   internal   longer   female

Fertilisation happens when a male cell and a _____ cell join together. Humans produce _____ offspring than frogs because we look after them for _____ . In humans fertilisation is _____ .

KEY POINTS

- Fertilisation happens when a female cell and a male cell join together.

- Fertilisation can be internal or external.

- Humans have fewer offspring than frogs because humans look after them for longer.

HOW DOES FERTILISATION HAPPEN?

What the human reproductive organs do

A man's **reproductive organs** make sperm and place them inside a woman's body. The sperm are made inside the **testes**.

A woman's reproductive organs make eggs. Her reproductive organs also provide a place for fertilisation to happen and a safe place for the baby to grow. Eggs are made in the **ovaries**.

Sexual intercourse

For fertilisation to happen, the sperm must reach the egg.

During **sexual intercourse**, the man's **penis** becomes stiff. He pushes it into the woman's **vagina**. It is here that the sperm are released.

The sperm swim through the cervix, up the **uterus** and meet the egg in the **oviduct**. This is where fertilisation happens.

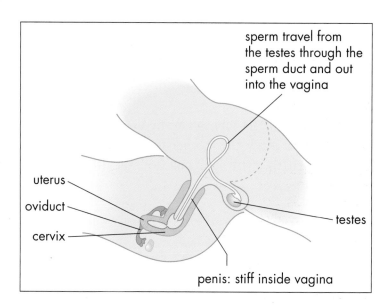

sperm travel from the testes through the sperm duct and out into the vagina

uterus

oviduct

cervix

testes

penis: stiff inside vagina

The reproductive systems

ⓐ **Copy or trace the picture of the male reproductive system.**

   Draw an arrow to show the path of the sperm after they leave the testis.

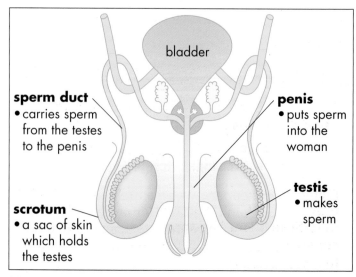

bladder

sperm duct
• carries sperm from the testes to the penis

penis
• puts sperm into the woman

testis
• makes sperm

scrotum
• a sac of skin which holds the testes

Male reproductive system

b Copy or trace the picture of the female reproductive system.

Draw an arrow to show the path of the sperm after they have been placed in the vagina.

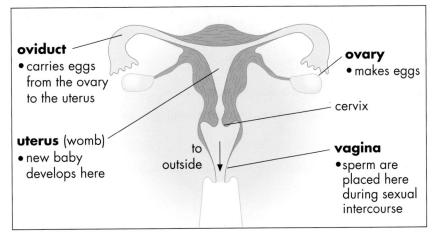

oviduct
• carries eggs from the ovary to the uterus

ovary
• makes eggs

cervix

uterus (womb)
• new baby develops here

to outside

vagina
• sperm are placed here during sexual intercourse

Female reproductive system

How egg and sperm cells do their job

Egg cells do not need to move. This means that they can be very large and contain food for the growing baby.

Sperm cells need a tail to swim. They need a streamlined shape and a head that can push its way into the egg cell.

large size
• contains a lot of food for the new baby's cells

nucleus
• contains information to control the new baby's cells

Egg cell

strengthened head
• contains chemicals which break open the egg's membrane

tail
• pushes the sperm towards the egg

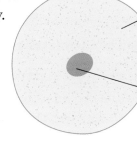

streamlined shape
• helps it move more easily and quickly

nucleus
• contains information to control the new baby's cells

Sperm cell

QUESTIONS

Copy these sentences and fill in the spaces using the words below:

eggs   food   large   sperm
streamlined   swim   tail

Males make _____ in their testes and females make _____ . The sperm _____ to the eggs to fertilise them. The egg is _____ and contains _____ . The sperm is _____ and has a _____ .

KEY POINTS

● Male reproductive organs make sperm and place the sperm inside the female.

● Female reproductive organs make eggs and feed and protect the baby.

● Sperm have a tail to swim to the egg.

● Eggs are large and contain food.

After fertilisation

When a sperm fertilises an egg it makes a new cell. This is the first cell of a new human being.

The fertilised cell now starts to divide. One cell divides into two cells. Two cells divide into four cells. These divisions happen over and over again.

It is surprising how quickly the number of cells increases as they continue to divide.

a **Take a piece of paper and tear it in half. Put the two halves together and tear them in half. Keep repeating this and see how many times you can tear the paper.**

You will be surprised how few tears it takes before you have lots of pieces.

Soon the fertilised cell has turned into a ball of cells. This ball of cells is called an **embryo**. The embryo passes down the oviduct and into the uterus.

Once inside the uterus, the embryo burrows into the uterus lining. This is called **implantation**. The woman is now **pregnant**.

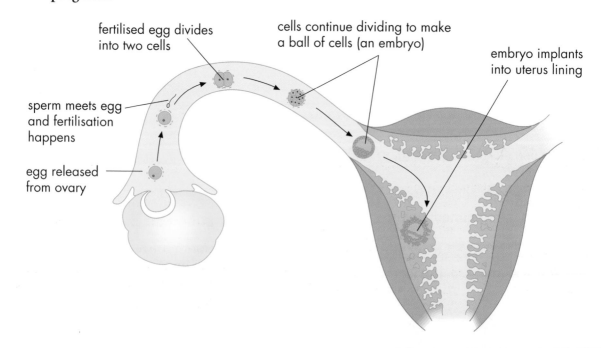

fertilised egg divides into two cells

cells continue dividing to make a ball of cells (an embryo)

embryo implants into uterus lining

sperm meets egg and fertilisation happens

egg released from ovary

How twins are made

Identical twins

Look at picture **A**. Sometimes the embryo splits into two balls of cells before it implants itself in the lining of the uterus. When this happens, the two new embryos will grow into two babies who look the same. We call these **identical twins**.

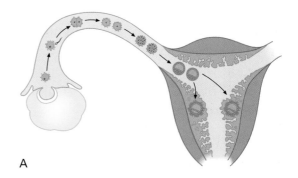

A

Non-identical twins

Look at picture **B**. Sometimes the mother will release two eggs into the oviduct instead of just one. If both of the eggs get fertilised, they will grow into two babies who look completely different. They may even be different sexes. We call these **non-identical twins**.

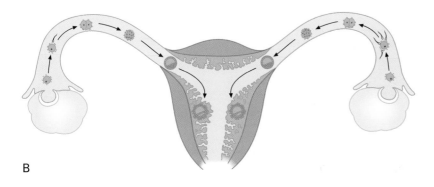

B

QUESTIONS

Copy these sentences and fill in the spaces using the words below:

embryo   implants   pregnant   uterus

A fertilised egg divides to form a ball of cells called an _____ . The embryo _____ into the lining of the _____ . The woman is then _____ .

KEY POINTS

- The fertilised egg divides to form an embryo.

- The embryo implants into the lining of the uterus and grows into the baby.

THE MENSTRUAL CYCLE

Ovulation

When a baby girl is born, she has thousands of eggs stored in her **ovaries**. When she is about 10 to 14 years of age, she will start releasing these eggs into her oviducts. This is called **ovulation**. Ovulation happens about once every 28 days.

Sometimes the egg will be fertilised and grow into a baby. Usually the egg will not be fertilised and it will not grow into a baby.

ⓐ **A woman is born with lots of eggs in her ovaries. Will they all be fertilised?**

The menstrual cycle

Each month, the uterus gets ready to receive a fertilised egg. The lining of the uterus gets thicker and has a very good blood supply. If the egg is not fertilised, the lining of the uterus breaks down.

The unfertilised egg, and all the tissue and blood lining the uterus, pass out of the girl's body. This is called **menstruation**, or having a **period**. It usually lasts for about four or five days.

Once the uterus lining has passed out of the girl's body, the whole process starts all over again. This is called the **menstrual cycle** and it repeats itself about every 28 days.

How many babies can be made at once?

Normally one egg is released every 28 days. This means that one baby is produced at a time.

Sometimes two eggs can be released. This is very rare. If both of them are fertilised, non-identical twins will be born.

ⓑ **How many eggs are released when non-identical twins are made?**

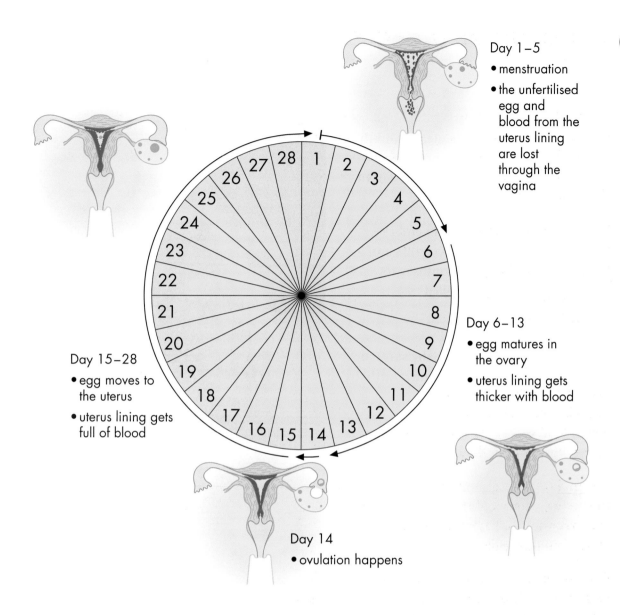

Day 1–5
- menstruation
- the unfertilised egg and blood from the uterus lining are lost through the vagina

Day 6–13
- egg matures in the ovary
- uterus lining gets thicker with blood

Day 15–28
- egg moves to the uterus
- uterus lining gets full of blood

Day 14
- ovulation happens

QUESTIONS

Look at the picture above.

1 On what day in the cycle does ovulation happen?

2 During which days in the cycle does menstruation take place?

3 How many days does the cycle last for?

KEY POINTS

- The menstrual cycle is a girl's body preparing itself for pregnancy.

- Menstruation occurs about every 28 days.

- Normally, only one egg is released at a time.

What is pregnancy?

After an egg has been fertilised it implants itself into the lining of the uterus, and the menstrual cycle stops. If menstruation continued, the embryo would pass out of the body.

When a woman is carrying an embryo, she is pregnant. The embryo grows and develops for about nine months before the baby is born. This is called the **gestation period**.

a Why do you think the baby stays in the mother's body for nine months?

The placenta

Because the embryo is inside the mother's body, it cannot eat or breathe like we do. It cannot even go to the toilet. The embryo has to get all of its food and oxygen from its mother's blood. All of the embryo's waste, such as carbon dioxide, has to be returned to its mother's blood.

To do this, the embryo's blood supply is connected to the wall of the uterus by a long tube called the **umbilical cord**. At the end of the umbilical cord is an organ called the **placenta**.

Food and oxygen can pass across the placenta from the mother's blood to the baby's blood. Carbon dioxide can pass across the placenta from the baby's blood into the mother's blood.

How the baby is protected

After about eight weeks, the baby is surrounded by a bag of fluid. This fluid is called the **amniotic fluid** and it protects the baby from bumps and knocks.

Most women also try to protect the baby by not putting poisonous substances into their blood. If the mother smokes or drinks alcohol, harmful substances can pass into the baby's blood. This can damage the baby and slow down its growth.

b **Why is it important not to smoke or drink alcohol when you are pregnant?**

Pregnant mothers should also try to avoid catching Rubella. Rubella is also called German measles. The disease makes poisons that can damage the baby's brain.

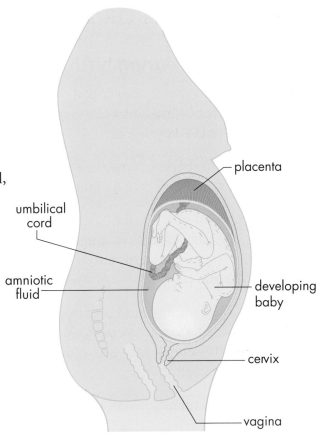

A developing baby inside a pregnant woman

QUESTIONS

Copy these sentences and fill in the spaces using the words below:

nine   oxygen   placenta   umbilical   uterus

Pregnancy lasts for about _____ months. It starts when an embryo implants in the _____ . Food and _____ can pass across the _____ from the mother's blood to the baby's. The baby is connected to the placenta by the _____ cord.

KEY POINTS

- Pregnancy happens when a mother is carrying an embryo.

- The placenta allows food and oxygen to pass from the mother's blood to the baby's blood.

WHAT DO NEWBORN BABIES NEED?

What happens during birth?

About nine months after fertilisation, the baby is ready to be born. The baby turns around in the uterus so that its head is facing downwards.

The muscles in the uterus **contract** and start to push the baby downwards. This is called **labour**.

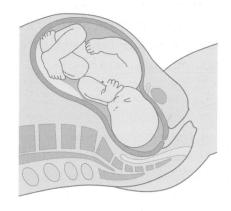

The bag of fluid around the baby bursts. This is sometimes called the '**waters breaking**'. Eventually the baby is pushed out of the uterus through the vagina. This is called **birth**.

The doctor clamps the umbilical cord in two places. This is so that when the cord is cut, the baby does not lose any blood. The cord is then tied off in a knot. This is what makes our 'belly button'.

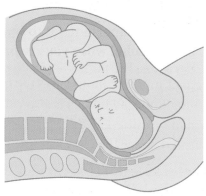

After about twenty minutes the placenta passes out of the vagina with the rest of the umbilical cord. This is sometimes called the **afterbirth**.

ⓐ **What happens to the placenta after the baby is born?**

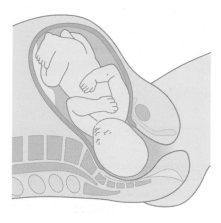

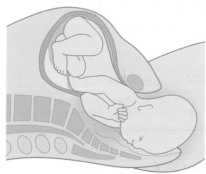

Babies are sometimes born early

Sometimes babies are born before nine months. Babies born early are called **premature**. To help the baby survive it is put into an **incubator**.

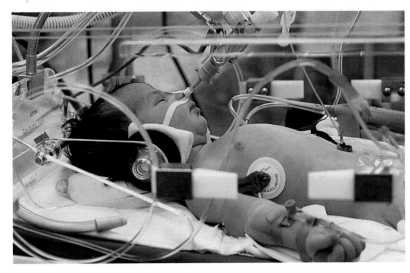

Inside an incubator is very similar to the inside of the mother's body. The temperature is the same and the baby is fed through a tube called a 'drip'.

ⓑ **What are babies born early called?**

Mothers make milk

A mother's breasts make milk for the baby to feed on. The mother's milk contains all the things that the baby needs. It can even protect the baby from disease. This is why doctors and midwives say that mother's milk is better than bottled milk.

QUESTIONS

Copy these sentences and fill in the spaces using the words below:

placenta   contractions   labour

milk   premature

Birth starts when _____ occur in the uterus. This is called _____ . About twenty minutes after the baby is born the _____ passes out of the vagina. If the baby is born early it is called _____ . The mother produces _____ to feed her baby.

KEY POINTS

- If a baby is born early it is called premature. It is cared for in an incubator.

- The mother makes milk to feed her baby.

HOW DO HUMANS CHANGE AS THEY GROW?

How children grow

Growth happens when a living thing increases in size. We measure growth by looking at people's height or their mass. Human growth occurs in spurts. At some ages humans grow quickly. At other ages humans grow slowly.

Boys and girls grow at different ages. Don't worry if you are bigger or smaller than your classmates. Fortunately we are all different. If we all grew at the same speed we would look like a race of robots.

How children develop

Children **develop** when they change from a boy to a man or a girl to a woman. We call this period of time **adolescence**. It usually occurs between the ages of 10 and 18. It involves physical and emotional changes.

Physical changes

Physical changes usually happen first. The reproductive organs start to get bigger. The person's appearance also starts to change. These physical changes are called **puberty**. They are shown on the opposite page.

ⓐ **Write down two physical changes that happen in puberty for boys and two for girls.**

Emotional changes

During adolescence, emotions start to change. People start to be attracted to the opposite sex. Some people become very moody and easily upset. But these emotions soon settle down as the boy changes into a man and the girl into a woman.

Physical changes in boys:

- Hair grows on the face and body.
- Pubic and underarm hair grows.
- Voice becomes deeper.
- Muscles develop.
- Penis enlarges.

Physical changes in girls:

- Hips get wider.
- Pubic and underarm hair grows.
- Breasts begin to grow.
- Menstruation starts.

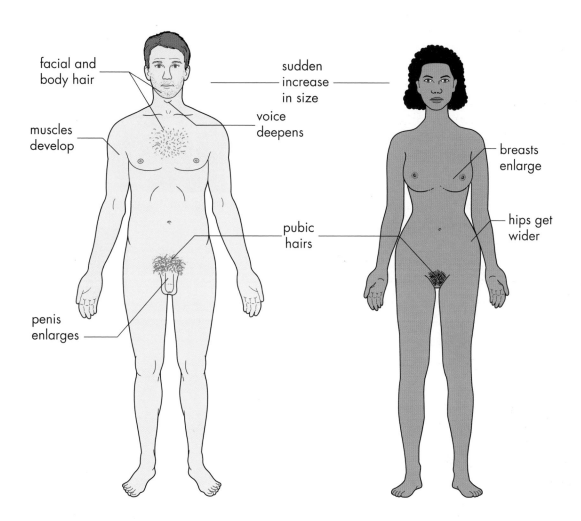

facial and body hair

muscles develop

penis enlarges

sudden increase in size

voice deepens

pubic hairs

breasts enlarge

hips get wider

QUESTIONS

Copy these sentences and fill in the spaces using the words below:

    adolescence   boys and girls   puberty

Physical and emotional changes occur during
_____ . They occur at different times in
_____ . The physical changes that occur
during adolescence are called _____ .

KEY POINTS

- Boys and girls grow at different speeds.

- Adolescence happens when boys become men and girls become women.

- Physical and emotional changes happen during adolescence.

C Environment and feeding relationships

C1 ADAPTING TO THE ENVIRONMENT

Habitats are different

The place where an animal or a plant lives is called its **habitat**. There are many different kinds of habitats. Some are hot and some are cold. Some are light and some are dark. Some are wet and some are dry.

The differences between the different habitats are called **environmental factors**.

Woodland

ⓐ Look at the two pictures. Write down two different environmental factors for each habitat.

Different animals and plants live in different habitats

Different types of living thing live in different habitats. Fish live in water and a cactus lives in a desert. We say fish are **adapted** to live in water and the cactus is adapted to live in the desert.

Desert

Living in water

Fish are adapted to live in water. They have a **streamlined** shape. They have fins and a tail to push them through the water. Because they live in water, fish do not breathe like we do. They need **gills** to be able to breathe in water.

ⓑ How are fish adapted to live in water?

Living in the air

Blackbirds can fly. They live in gardens and woodlands. They have large wings and a tail that help them to fly. They can also change direction very quickly to avoid hitting trees.

Blackbirds have a streamlined shape to help them move through the air. They have claws so that they can grip onto tree branches. They have a pointed beak for catching food like insects and worms.

c **How are blackbirds adapted to live in the air?**

All animals and plants are adapted to live in their own habitat.

Look at the picture of the mole. It burrows and lives underground.

d **Write down how the mole may be adapted to live underground.**

QUESTIONS

Copy these sentences and fill in the spaces using the words below:

     adapted   environmental   habitat

The place where an animal or a plant lives is called a _____ . The differences between habitats are called _____ factors. Animals and plants are _____ to live in their own habitat.

KEY POINTS

- Habitats are different from each other.

- These differences are called environmental factors.

- Animals and plants are adapted to live in a particular habitat.

ADAPTING TO DAILY CHANGES IN THE ENVIRONMENT

How habitats change

Habitats change every day. Think about the habitat around your school.

Noise

When all the students arrive it is very noisy. But by the start of the first lesson it is quiet again. During break and lunch times it gets noisy again.

Light and temperature

At night it is dark and cool around the school. But as the sun rises, it gets lighter and warmer. When the sun sets in the evening, it gets darker and colder again.

The red line on the graph shows how the light changes over 24 hours. It shows the strength or intensity of the light at different times.

ⓐ Look at the graph. What time did it start to get light?

ⓑ Look at the graph again. What time did it start to get dark?

ⓒ When was the light the brightest?

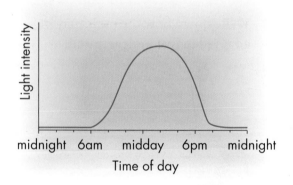

Wet and dry

Not all changes happen at the same times each day. Some days it might rain a lot. Other days it might not rain at all.

Changing habitats

Animals and plants are adapted to cope with changes in their habitats. Some flowers open during the day when the sun shines on them and close again at night when it is dark.

Animals like foxes and mice come out at night. Perhaps a fox visits your school grounds. But it would only visit at night when it is dark and quiet.

How animals choose

You can investigate how animals choose which environment to live in by using a **choice chamber**. The picture on the right shows a choice chamber. It is called a choice chamber because it gives the animals a choice of where to go.

The filter paper on the left is damp. The filter paper on the right is dry. If you put some woodlice in the chamber you could time how long they spend on each side of the chamber.

(d) **How would you set up a choice chamber to see if woodlice preferred light or dark?**

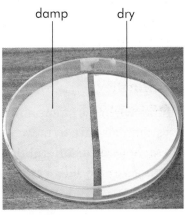

damp   dry

A choice chamber

QUESTIONS

1 Write down two ways that the habitat in your bedroom changes every day.

2 What would you do if your habitat became very cold?

KEY POINTS

- Habitats change every day.

- Animals and plants are adapted to these changes.

Why living things change during the year

In the winter we wear thicker coats and spend most of our time inside. In the summer we wear shorts and spend a lot of time outside. We change our behaviour to cope with changes in the **environment**.

Look at the two pictures of a garden. One was taken in the winter. The other was taken during the summer.

ⓐ **Write down two differences between the pictures.**

Living things usually change when there is a change in temperature, a change in the amount of light or a change in how easy it is to find food and water.

How living things change during the year

Migrations

Sometimes when the environment changes, animals have to move. We call these movements **migrations**. The picture shows wildebeest. They live in Africa and travel hundreds of miles in search of grass for food.

ⓑ **Can you think of any other animal that migrates each year?**

Dormant

Some insects spend the winter inside a protective case. The case protects them from harsh weather. When an insect is inside its protective case, we say that it is **dormant** for the winter.

In the spring, the insect comes out of its protective case. The picture shows a butterfly coming out of its protective case in the spring.

Plants can also become dormant in winter.

c How do trees become dormant in the winter?

Hibernation

Some animals, like bears, go to sleep for the whole of the winter. They only wake up when the spring arrives. This is called **hibernation**.

Hedgehogs hibernate in the winter. They sleep under piles of leaves. This is why we should be careful when we light bonfires on bonfire night. A hedgehog may have gone to sleep in the middle of the bonfire.

d Can you think of any other animal that hibernates?

QUESTIONS

Copy these sentences and fill in the spaces using the words below:

dormant   environment   hibernate   migrate

Living things change their behaviour when the _____ changes. Some animals _____ in search of food. Insects go _____ in a protective case. Hedgehogs _____ in a deep sleep until spring.

KEY POINTS

- Animals and plants change their behaviour when the environment changes.

- Some animals migrate in search of food.

- Some animals and plants become dormant in the winter.

PREDATORS AND PREY

What are predators and prey?

Animals that eat other animals are called **predators**. The animals that they eat are called **prey**.

A lion is a predator. The zebra that the lion eats is its prey.

predator

ⓐ Can you think of any other predators?

ⓑ Can you think of any other prey?

A cow is not a predator because it does not hunt and kill other animals. The grass is not its prey. Only animals can be prey.

prey

Predators are good at hunting for food

Predators are adapted to hunt food. The kestrel has eyes that point forward. This makes it easier for it to judge distances. It has sharp claws to catch its prey.

A spider spins a sticky web to trap the fly.

The tiger is hard to see. It has camouflage.

ⓒ Can you think how the tiger is adapted to hunt prey?

Prey are good at not being eaten

Rabbits have eyes at the sides of their heads. This lets them see all around for predators coming.

d **What else has the rabbit got that will tell it when predators are coming?**

Some prey, like this tortoise, have a 'suit of armour' to protect them.

e **Can you think of anything else that has a hard outer shell for protection?**

QUESTIONS

Copy these sentences and fill in the spaces using the words below:

adapted   eyes   claws   predator   prey

A lion is a _____ and a zebra is its _____ .
A kestrel has sharp _____ to hold its prey, but a rabbit has _____ on the sides of its head to see the kestrel coming. Predators are _____ to catch prey. Prey are adapted to escape from a _____ .

KEY POINTS

- Predators eat other animals.

- Prey get eaten by other animals.

- Predators are adapted for catching prey.

- Prey are adapted to escape from predators.

C5 FOOD CHAINS AND FOOD WEBS

Where plants and animals get their food

Plants make their own food. They use energy from sunlight. Because they produce their food, they are called **producers**. Animals eat or consume food. Animals are called **consumers**.

Some animals eat only plants. These animals are called **herbivores**. Other animals eat only meat. They are called **carnivores**.

Food chains

A **food chain** is a way of showing what eats what. A food chain always starts with a plant and ends with a carnivore. We can draw a food chain like this:

grass ⟶ rabbit ⟶ fox

Look at the picture. It shows some examples of food chains.

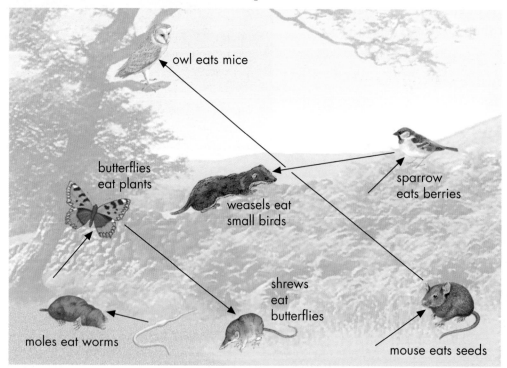

owl eats mice

butterflies eat plants

sparrow eats berries

weasels eat small birds

shrews eat butterflies

moles eat worms

mouse eats seeds

ⓐ Write out two food chains you can see in the picture.

ⓑ Write the name of a carnivore and the name of a herbivore in the picture.

Energy in food chains

Food chains do not only tell us what eats what. They also show how energy is passed from one living thing to another. The arrows show which direction the energy is moving.

grass ⟶ rabbit ⟶ fox

- Grass uses energy from the Sun to make its food and grow. The energy becomes stored in the grass.

- The rabbit eats the grass. It uses some of the energy to move about and some of the energy to grow. Some of the energy becomes stored in the rabbit.

- The fox eats the rabbit. It uses some of the energy stored in the rabbit to move about and the rest to grow.

Food webs

Animals do not just eat one thing. Animals eat lots of different things. To show this, we draw a **food web**.

C **Look at the food web.**
Write down two animals that eat the same food.

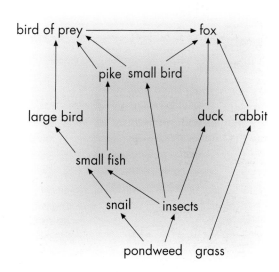

QUESTIONS

Copy these sentences and fill in the spaces using the words below:

   carnivores   consumers

   herbivores   producers

Plants make food and are called _____ . All animals are called _____ . Animals that eat plants are also called _____ . Animals that eat other animals are called _____ .

- Food chains show what eats what.

- Food chains show how energy moves from one living thing to another.

C6 FOOD WEB DETECTIVES

Finding out what lives where

Do you know all of the animals and plants that live around your school? You probably know a few of them. There will be many that you do not know. There will also be many that you have never seen. Some of them hide away and are difficult to see.

How to find animals

There are many different ways to find hidden animals. Here are a few of them. Try using some of them to find animals hidden around your school.

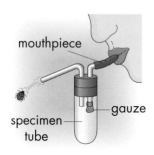

Pooters: Have a close look at the plants and trees. Suck up any animals you can find into the tube.

Tree beating: Spread a big sheet out under a tree. Shake the branches and see which animals fall onto the sheet.

Sweep netting: If your garden has long grass, sweep the net backwards and forwards. Any insects get knocked off the grass and into your net.

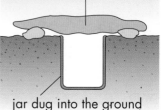

Pit-fall traps: After a few hours, you should find a little group of insects in the bottom.

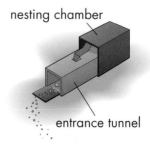

Small mammal traps: Put a trail of bait leading into the trap. If an animal goes in, the door will close behind it. Make sure you check the traps regularly or the animal may die of cold.

ⓐ Why do you think animals tend to hide away?

ⓑ Can you think of any other ways of finding animals?

Remember – we are looking for animals in their habitat. They should be disturbed as little as possible and not harmed.

How to work out what eats what

It is not always easy to see what eats what because animals hide away when humans are around. To find out what eats what, we have to look for clues.

Owl's droppings are called pellets. We can open the pellets and recognise the little bones of the animals that the owl has eaten.

Greenfly are found on rose bushes.

ⓒ **What do you think greenfly eat?**

Thrushes pick up snails in their beaks. They break the shells against a hard stone. If you find a stone next to lots of broken snail shells, you know who has eaten them.

QUESTIONS

Copy these sentences and fill in the spaces using the words below:

> care   pooter   shake

To collect insects from a tree I would gently _____ a branch. To collect insects that I can see close up, I would use a _____ . The animals that I collect should always be treated with _____ .

KEY POINTS

- Many more animals live in a habitat than we can see.

- We have to use clues to discover what eats what.

D Variation and classification

D1 VARIATION

Looking different

Some types of living things look very alike. All dogs look like dogs and all humans look like humans.

But all dogs also look different from each other and all humans look different from each other. It is these differences that allow us to recognise different people.

These differences are called **variation**.

a Look at the pictures of the two dogs.
Write down three differences between them.

Humans differ from each other in many ways.
Here are a few:

- hair colour
- eye colour
- ear size
- height
- mass

Showing the difference

We can use graphs to show some of the differences between animals and plants more clearly.

Some students decided to find out the different eye colours of students in their class:

1 They recorded the eye colour of twenty-six students on a tally chart like the one opposite:

2 They found three eye colours: blue, brown and green.

3 They used the information in the tally chart to draw a bar chart like the one opposite:

Look at the chart.

b **What is the most common eye colour?**

c **What is the least common eye colour?**

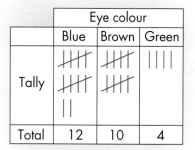

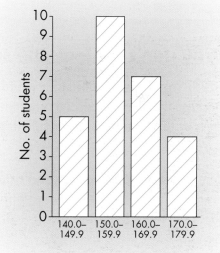

Eye colour

The students then decided to find out how the height of students in their class varied.

1 They divided the class into four groups depending on their height.

2 They recorded the height of each student on a tally chart and then used the information to draw a bar chart like the one opposite:

d **What is the most common height of students in the class?**

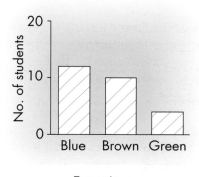

Height (cm)

QUESTIONS

Copy these sentences and fill in the spaces using the words below:

size   eyes   variation

Humans differ from each other in _____ of ears and colour of _____ . These differences are called _____ .

KEY POINTS

- Differences between the same types of living thing are called variation.

WHAT CAUSES VARIATION?

Why do families look different?

Have you ever been told that you have your mother's eyes, or your father's nose? Children often look a little like their parents. This is because they get, or **inherit**, many features from their parents.

Look at the family tree.

The boy has inherited curly hair from his mother and big ears from his dad.

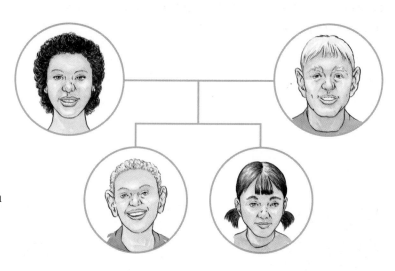

a Who did the girl inherit her black hair from?

Why don't we look the same as our brothers and sisters?

Brothers and sisters look different from each other because they have inherited different features from each of their parents. This is called **inherited variation**.

The only time that brothers and sisters look the same is when they are identical twins. This is because identical twins inherit the same features from their parents.

Plants inherit features from their parents as well. Different flower colours and different leaf shapes are good examples of inherited variation in plants.

b Why do brothers and sisters almost never look exactly like each other?

Growing up differently

When identical twins get older, even they begin to look different from each other. For example, one twin may do weight training and have bigger muscles. One twin may go on holiday and get a sun-tan.

These differences are caused by the environment and are not inherited from their parents. They are caused by things around them and are called **environmental variation.**

Look at the pictures of the two trees.

One tree has grown in a very windy environment. The other has not.

G **Which tree do you think has grown in the windy environment?**

QUESTIONS

Copy these sentences and fill in the spaces using the words below:

    inherited   environmental

Eye colour is an example of _____ variation.

Hair length is an example of _____ variation.

KEY POINTS

- Variation can be inherited, for example hair colour.

- Variation can be due to the environment, for example a sun-tan.

HOW CAN WE DESCRIBE LIVING THINGS?

Describing the differences between living things

Different animals and plants look and behave very differently. There is a lot of variation between them.

Jenny loves to ride horses. Look at one of the pages from her diary.

Writing, like Jenny's diary, does not always describe an animal perfectly. She could easily be talking about her pet dog rather than her horse. A dog is a very different animal to a horse.

My diary
… he is very strong but always does as he is told.
Today he jumped a fence for the first time.
My dad says he is a very intelligent animal and that he should be easy to train.
He is brown in colour, but this may change as he gets older.
The vet is coming today to check him over.

a **How would you describe a horse to someone who had never seen one before?**

Describing differences accurately

To help someone tell the difference between two animals, we need to describe each animal very accurately. To do this we need to count and measure the different features of each animal. Look at how we record information about the honeybee in the table.

Body parts	Legs	Antennae	Wings	Tail
How many?	6	2	2 pairs	no
How big?	up to 1 cm	short	1 cm	—
What colour?	black	black	grey	—

Variation and classification

Trying to describe differences in fish

Look at the picture of the fish.

Now look at the table that describes one of the fish.

Body parts	Fins	Skin	Nose	Tail
How many?	1	—	—	yes
How big?	large	—	long	small
What colour?	grey	grey	grey	grey

ⓑ Draw the fish described in the table.

ⓒ Now choose one of the other fish and fill in a copy of this table for it.

KEY POINTS

- Differences between living things have to be described accurately.

QUESTIONS

Some aliens arrive on Earth. They have never seen a cat before. Copy and complete the following table to help them recognise a cat.

Body parts	Whiskers	Legs	Fur length	Mouth/teeth
How many?				
How big?				
What colour?				

HOW CAN WE SORT LIVING THINGS INTO GROUPS?

Sorting out living things

There are millions of different living things in the world. Even scientists find it hard to identify all of them. To make it easier, scientists put them into groups according to the different features each has. This is called **classifying**.

If two animals have lots of features in common, they go into the same group, even though they are not exactly the same. We can see how this works by looking at human fingerprints.

Fingerprints can be used to identify criminals because no one has the same fingerprints as anyone else. Although the fingerprints are different, they still have some things in common. They can be put into two different groups, A and B.

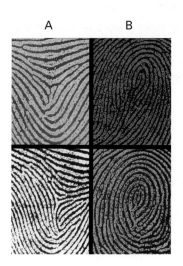

ⓐ Draw a feature which group A have, but group B do not.

ⓑ Look at the pictures of the leaves. Some leaves are whole, while others are divided up into sections. Draw the leaves and put them into two separate groups depending upon the shape of the leaves.

Naming the groups

If living things have lots of features in common, scientists put them into a group called a **species**. Groups like humans, cats and dogs are all species.

C **All the animals shown below are different species. How many species can you name?**

But each plant or animal in the same species usually looks a little different from the rest, just like fingerprints are different but similar. This is why we can tell one person from another even though we are all part of the same species.

QUESTIONS

Copy these sentences and fill in the spaces using the words below:

> species   classifying   features

Sorting living things into groups is called _____. Groups like humans, cats and dogs are all different _____. Species are groups that have lots of _____ in common.

KEY POINTS

- Classification is sorting things into groups.

- A species is a group that has lots of features in common.

WHY DO SCIENTISTS CLASSIFY LIVING THINGS?

Why do we put things into groups?

Humans like classifying. We often put things into groups without even realising it.

There is usually a very good reason why we do this.

Look at the pictures of the nails and screws.

They are both used for fixing things together. But they fix things in different ways and most people would put them into two separate jars. In other words, they have classified them.

Nails

Screws

Why classify living things?

Scientists classify living things because:

1 It makes it easier to tell other scientists about a particular species. For example, if we say 'a six-inch nail', it is clearer than saying 'one of those fixing things'.
2 If they find a living thing that they have not seen before, they can put it into one of the groups and this helps them understand it.
3 It helps us see how closely related two different species are. For example, humans are more closely related to chimps than to snakes because humans and chimps have lots of features in common.

ⓐ **Give one reason why scientists like to classify living things.**

A scientist called Carl Linnaeus was the first person to give each species a name. He used a language called Latin. Scientists all over the world use the same Latin names today.

ⓑ **Why is it important for a scientist in China and a scientist in England to use the same Latin name to describe an animal?**

Dandelion (*Taraxacum officinale*)

Plants and animals

Even sorting living things into species leaves us with millions of species. It makes things easier to handle if we have some bigger groups.

To help classify living things, scientists put them into large groups called **kingdoms**. All animal species belong to the animal kingdom. All plant species belong to the plant kingdom.

Animals

What are the differences between animals and plants?

The main differences between animals and plants are that:

- plants can make their own food while animals have to eat plants or other animals to get food
- animals can move from place to place to find food while plants do not.

C Copy out the following list of living things. Against each one write down '*animal kingdom*' or '*plant kingdom*'.

Plants

> **lion   oak tree   human   daffodil**
> **rose   cat   dog**

QUESTIONS

Copy these sentences and fill in the spaces using the words below:

kingdoms   Latin   species   understand

Scientists classify living things because it helps them _____ them. They use _____ names for different _____ of plants and animals so that scientists from different countries can all understand each other. Plants and animals belong to two different _____ .

KEY POINTS

- Two big groups of living things are the animal and plant kingdoms.

D5

HOW DO SCIENTISTS CLASSIFY ANIMALS?

How can we divide the animal kingdom into smaller groups?

We can group together animal species that are similar to each other. For example, all those animals with a backbone are one group and all those without a backbone are another group.

Animals with a backbone are called **vertebrates**.
Animals without a backbone are called **invertebrates**.

Vertebrates

Vertebrates can be divided into five smaller groups. Each species in a group has similar features. The pictures below show what those features are.

a Look at the pictures below. Copy the table and put the features of each group in it. The first one has been done for you.

Group name	Skin type	Lungs or gills	Babies or eggs	Water or land
birds	feathers	lungs	eggs	land

Fish: Gills, fins, scales, streamlined body, live and lay eggs in water.

Amphibians: Soft, wet skin, lungs, live in water or on land, lay eggs in water.

Birds: Feathers, lungs, wings, lay eggs with a shell.

Mammals: Hair or fur, lungs, babies develop inside mother, babies fed on milk from mother.

Reptiles: Dry skin covered in scales, lungs, lay eggs with a shell, live on land.

How can we divide invertebrates into smaller groups?

Invertebrates can also be divided into smaller groups.
Each species in a group has features in common. Look
at the pictures to see what those features are.

Insects – body divided into three sections,
three pairs of jointed legs, antennae,
two pairs of wings, body covered by
a hard case.

Example – housefly

Molluscs – soft body covered by a
shell, live in water and on land.

Example – snail

Arachnids – body divided into
two sections, four pairs of jointed
legs, antennae, body covered by
a hard case.

Example – spider

QUESTIONS

1 Copy out the following list of animals.
   After each animal write down the word
   vertebrate or *invertebrate*.

   lion   frog   snail   fish
   housefly   spider   snake   bird

2 Copy out the following list of vertebrates.
   After each animal write down the word *fish*,
   amphibian, *bird*, *reptile* or *mammal*.

   newt   sparrow   shark
   kangaroo   tortoise

KEY POINTS

- The animal kingdom can be
  divided into the vertebrates
  and the invertebrates.

- The vertebrates can be
  divided into five smaller
  groups.

- The invertebrates can also be
  divided into smaller groups.

- Each group has similar
  features in common.

E Acids and alkalis

WHAT ARE ACIDS AND ALKALIS?

Acids and alkalis

Acids and alkalis are two groups of chemicals. We find acids and alkalis in our everyday lives.

Where we find acids

People think that **acids** are very dangerous. Some of them are. But others are not. Some acids are found in our food and are very important to us.

ⓐ **Look at the picture. All the things shown contain acids. Make a list of the things that contain acids in this picture.**

Where we find alkalis

Alkalis are also important to us. Just like acids, some of them are dangerous and some of them are not.

ⓑ **Look at the picture. All the products shown contain alkalis. Make a list of the things that contain alkalis in this picture.**

You can find lots of acids and alkalis just by looking around your home. Most foods are slightly acidic or alkaline. It helps to give them taste.

Acidic foods, such as lemon juice, tend to have a sharp or sour taste.

ⓒ **Make a list of foods that have a sharp or sour taste.**

We even find acids and alkalis in our own bodies. Acid in your stomach helps you digest food and kill **bacteria**. If you have too much acid it causes acid indigestion.

How we know if acids and alkalis are dangerous

It is important to know if an acid or an alkali is safe or dangerous so that we know how to handle it. Many of the acids and alkalis in our homes are perfectly safe. But some of them are very dangerous.

We can tell the dangerous ones because they always have a **hazard symbol** on the container. This means they are very strong acids or alkalis.

The same symbols are used in all sorts of places. You may see them around your school. They are even used on lorries that carry acids and alkalis around the country.

Hazard symbols	Definitions
Harmful	Can make you ill if swallowed, breathed in or absorbed through the skin
Irritant	May cause reddening or blistering of the skin
Corrosive	Attacks and destroys living tissue, including eyes and skin

d **Look at the pictures of the hazard symbols. Next to the picture it tells you how the acid or alkali might harm you. Which is more dangerous, an irritant or a corrosive acid or alkali?**

e **Vinegar and lemons are both acidic. Why don't they have a hazard symbol on them?**

Staying safe

- Always treat unknown chemicals with respect.
- Look for hazard symbols.
- If you get any on your skin, wash it off immediately.

QUESTIONS

1 Write down the names of two substances shown on these pages that contain safe acids.

2 Write down the names of two substances shown on these pages that contain safe alkalis.

KEY POINTS

- Acids and alkalis are found all around us.
- Some are dangerous but many are safe and useful.
- Dangerous ones should have a hazard symbol on the container.

Telling acids from alkalis

Because acids and alkalis often look the same, we cannot tell which they are just by looking at them. Some of them are colourless liquids and look just like water. To tell whether a substance is an acid or an alkali we need to use an **indicator**.

The indicator will change to one colour in an acid, and a different colour in an alkali.

Where indicators come from

Many indicators come from plants. Some plants have juices that change to one colour in an acid and to a different colour in an alkali. By adding a drop of the plant juice to a substance, the colour change will tell us if the substance is an acid or an alkali.

Here are some examples.

	Red cabbage	Beetroot	Blackcurrant
In acid			
In alkali			

Look at the pictures.

ⓐ What colour does blackcurrant turn in acids?

ⓑ What colour does beetroot turn in alkalis?

Indicators used in science lessons

We have even better indicators in science lessons. They change different colours in acids and alkalis. **Universal Indicator** will even tell us how strong or weak the acid or alkali is. Here are some of the different types of indicators used in science lessons.

Indicator	Litmus solution	Universal indicator	Phenolphthalein	Methyl orange
Colour in acid				
Colour in alkali				

c Look at the picture. What colour does Universal Indicator turn in alkalis?

Common acids and alkalis

The list below shows some of the acids and alkalis that we use in schools. These are not all the acids and alkalis. There are many others.

Acids	Alkalis
hydrochloric acid	ammonium hydroxide (ammonia solution)
sulphuric acid	sodium hydroxide (caustic soda)
nitric acid	calcium hydroxide (limewater)
citric acid	potassium hydroxide (caustic potash)

d Look at the picture above. What colour will Universal Indicator turn in hydrochloric acid?

QUESTIONS

Copy these sentences and fill in the spaces using the words below:

    same   indicators   juice

Chemicals that change colour in acids and alkalis are called _____ . We make them from the _____ of some plants. They are useful because acids and alkalis often look the _____ .

KEY POINTS

- Indicators change to different colours in acids and alkalis.

- Some plant juices can be used as indicators.

HOW STRONG ARE ACIDS AND ALKALIS?

The strength of acids and alkalis

Acids and alkalis have different strengths. For example, sulphuric acid can be very strong but cows' milk is a very weak acid.

It is important that we can measure the strength of acids and alkalis. Then we know if we have to take care when we handle them.

ⓐ **Why is it important that we know the strength of an acid?**

Lemon juice is a weak acid, but the acid in a car battery is a very strong acid.

Measuring the strength of acids and alkalis

To find out how strong an acid or alkali is we use **Universal Indicator** paper. This is sometimes called pH paper.

When you dip the pH paper into the solution of acid or alkali, it changes colour. You then compare the pH paper with a colour chart. This tells you how strong the acid or alkali is.

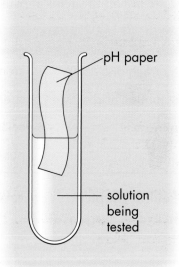

pH paper

solution being tested

The pH scale

Look at the colour chart on the next page. This chart is called the **pH scale**. Each colour has a different number. This number is its pH. The numbers range from 0 to 14.

Numbers under 7 are acids.

Numbers over 7 are alkalis.

The closer the number is to 7, the weaker the acid or alkali is. The farther the number is from 7, the stronger the acid or alkali is. Number 0 is a very strong acid. Number 14 is a very strong alkali.

pH chart

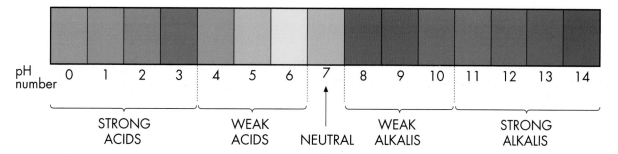

| pH number | 0 | 1 | 2 | 3 | 4 | 5 | 6 | 7 | 8 | 9 | 10 | 11 | 12 | 13 | 14 |

STRONG ACIDS   WEAK ACIDS   NEUTRAL   WEAK ALKALIS   STRONG ALKALIS

ⓑ Look at the colour of the paper in picture A, and find the same colour on the pH chart. Write down the pH number of the colour.

ⓒ Is this an acid or an alkali?

ⓓ How strong is it?

ⓔ Look at the colour of the paper in picture B, and find the same colour on the pH chart. Write down the pH number of the colour.

ⓕ Is this an acid or an alkali?

ⓖ How strong is it?

A

What does 'neutral' mean?

Things that are not acids or alkalis are **neutral**. Any solution that has a pH number of 7 is neutral. Pure water has a pH of 7.

ⓗ Is pure water an acid, an alkali, or neutral?

ⓘ What colour does Universal Indicator paper turn in pure water?

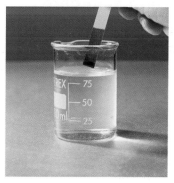

B

QUESTIONS

1 Copy these sentences and fill in the spaces using the words below:

> pH   neutral   Universal

The strength of acids and alkalis can be measured using _____ Indicator paper. The _____ scale is numbered from 0 to 14. Things that are not acids or alkalis are called _____ .

KEY POINTS

- The pH scale measures the strengths of acids and alkalis.

- We can find the pH by using Universal Indicator paper.

- Some substances, such as pure water, are neutral.

Acids and alkalis are useful

Millions of tonnes of acids and alkalis are used each year. They are used to make things like fertilisers, soaps, plastics, paints and drugs.

Preserving food

One way of preserving food is to put the food in an acid. Vinegar is an acid. When we put food in vinegar we call it pickling.

The picture shows some pickled walnuts. They will keep for a long time.

Hair and skin care

To keep our hair and skin in the best possible condition, it should be slightly acidic. It should be about pH 5.5. This is why some shampoos and soaps have pH 5.5 on the label.

Plant and insect stings

We sometimes get stung by bees or stinging nettles. It hurts because the bees or nettles inject acid into our skin.

We can treat the sting with calamine lotion or anti-sting cream. Both of these are slightly alkaline.

ⓐ Look at the picture of the nettle. How do you think it manages to sting you?

Nettle

Soil treatment

Some soil is too acidic to let the crops grow properly. The farmer adds lime to the soil. Lime makes the soil less acidic.

What happens when an acid is added to an alkali?

Acids and alkalis cancel each other out. This means that when the right amount of acid is added to an alkali, they become neutral. This is why the farmer adds lime to an acidic soil.

$$ACID + ALKALI = NEUTRAL$$

Acids have pH numbers lower than 7.

Alkalis have pH numbers higher than 7.

When acids and alkalis are added together, they produce a substance of pH 7. This is a neutral substance. It is not an acid. It is not an alkali.

ⓑ Bee stings are acidic. Why should you not rub vinegar on a bee sting?

ⓒ Wasp stings are alkaline. Why should you rub vinegar on a wasp sting?

QUESTIONS

Copy these sentences and fill in the spaces using the words below:

acid   alkali   neutral

You should rub an _____ onto a bee sting and an _____ onto a wasp sting. Acids and alkalis cancel each other out and become _____ .

KEY POINTS

- Acids and alkalis are useful.

- Acids and alkalis cancel each other out and become neutral.

Stomach acid can be a problem

Sometimes we get stomach ache. This may be because we have too much acid in our stomach. We call this acid indigestion.

ⓐ **Why is it not a good idea to eat lots of pickled onions if you have acid indigestion?**

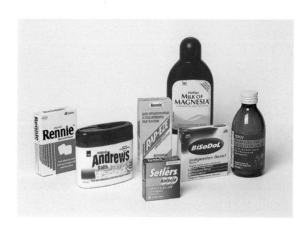

Look at the picture. It shows some of the things we can take for an acid stomach.

ⓑ **Make a list of some of the things we can take to cure acid indigestion.**

Medicines that neutralise stomach acids are called **antacids**. They are alkalis. It is not a good idea to take too many of them. Your stomach only works properly if it is slightly acidic.

ⓒ **Why do the medicines in the picture cure acid indigestion?**

How much antacid should we take?

It is difficult to know how much antacid we should take to cure our acid indigestion. We need to know how much acid each tablet of antacid cancels out or neutralises.

- If we take too few tablets, the stomach may be still too acidic.

- If we take too many tablets, the stomach may not be acidic enough.

We can measure how much antacid we need by carrying out an experiment.

How to find out how much antacid we need

Look at the picture. It shows how we can measure how much acid will be neutralised by an antacid tablet.

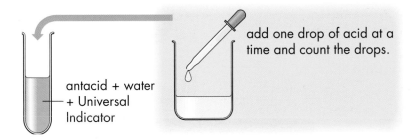

antacid + water
+ Universal
Indicator

add one drop of acid at a time and count the drops.

d We place the antacid in a test tube with some Universal Indicator. Look at the pH chart on page 57. What colour will the Universal Indicator turn?

We then add acid to the test tube, until the indicator shows that the solution is neutral. The amount of acid we add to the test tube is the amount of acid that is neutralised by one antacid tablet.

e Look at the pH chart on page 57 again. What colour would the Universal Indicator turn if you added too much acid?

QUESTIONS

Copy these sentences and fill in the spaces using the words below:

acid   alkaline   antacids   neutralise

We use _____ to treat acid indigestion. They are _____ and so they _____ too much stomach _____ . We should not neutralise all the _____ in our stomach because we need some acid for digestion.

KEY POINTS

- Antacids are alkalis. We use them to treat acid indigestion.

- We can measure how much acid is neutralised by an alkali.

F Simple chemical reactions

Changes

Things around us are changing all the time.

Lakes freeze over in the winter.

Coal turns to ashes when we burn it.

Types of change

When we look carefully at these changes, we find that there are two different kinds. Some changes can never change back. Other changes can be reversed.

Look at the pictures at the top of the page.

ⓐ **One of the changes cannot be reversed. Which one?**

Changes that cannot be reversed are called **chemical changes**. The change that has taken place is called a **chemical reaction**.

Looking at chemical reactions

Whenever a chemical change takes place, there must have been a chemical reaction. Many chemical reactions happen when we mix two or more substances together.

If you notice any of the following things happen when you add two substances together, you know that a chemical reaction has taken place.

Fizzing

Some chemicals fizz when you mix them together. Look at what happens when you add **bicarbonate of soda** to lemon juice.

Smelly

If a new smell appears when you mix two chemicals together, a chemical reaction has probably taken place.

Looks different

Chemicals often change colour when you mix them together.

When you put magnesium into blue copper sulphate, the blue colour disappears.

Hot or cold

Some chemicals go cold when mixed together. Others go hot. In an explosion, the chemical reactions are very fast and release a lot of heat as well as light.

ⓑ **Describe three things that would tell you when a chemical reaction had taken place.**

QUESTIONS

Which of the following are chemical reactions, and which are not?

     smelly change   bubbling change

         melting change

KEY POINTS

- Chemical reactions may happen when you mix two substances together.

- Chemical changes do not change back.

HOW DO ACIDS REACT WITH METALS?

Acids and corrosion

Some acids are **corrosive**. This means they will eat away or **corrode** other substances.

The picture shows what happens to an iron plate in a car when the car battery acid leaks.

When an acid reacts with a metal, a gas called **hydrogen** is given off. The gas floats away. This is why holes are left behind.

A test for hydrogen gas

Hydrogen gas is invisible. It has no smell. So how can we prove it is there? Luckily hydrogen has some unusual properties.

- **Hydrogen is lighter than air.**

This means a balloon filled with hydrogen floats upwards. It also means that if we keep hydrogen in a test tube, we have to turn the test tube upside down.

- **Hydrogen burns.**

If we light hydrogen, it burns very quickly. In the test tube it will burn with a squeaky 'pop'.

Even though we cannot see or smell hydrogen, this test proves that hydrogen is there.

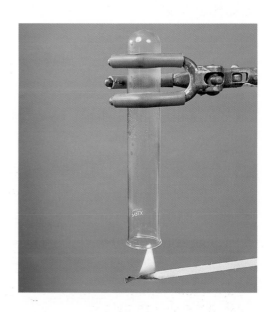

Acids reacting with metals

Some metals react with acids much faster than others. You can tell how quickly a metal reacts with an acid by looking for the number of bubbles. The more bubbles, the quicker the reaction.

Look at the picture. Acid has been added to four different metals.

| Calcium | Magnesium | Zinc | Iron |

ⓐ Which metal is reacting the most quickly with the acid?

ⓑ Which metal is reacting the slowest with the acid?

The gas in the bubbles is hydrogen. If we collect the gas, it will be lighter than air and burn with a squeaky 'pop'.

QUESTIONS

Copy these sentences and fill in the spaces using the words below:

burns   corrosive   faster   hydrogen   lighter

Some acids are _____. When they react with metals they release _____ gas. Hydrogen is _____ than air and _____ very easily. Acids react _____ with some metals than others.

KEY POINTS

- Some acids are corrosive.

- When acids react with metals, they release hydrogen gas.

- Acids react faster with some metals than others.

HOW DO ACIDS REACT WITH CARBONATES?

Carbon dioxide

Hydrogen is not the only invisible gas given off when acids react with other chemicals. **Carbon dioxide** is also invisible and has no smell. It is given off when acids react with chemicals called carbonates.

Just like hydrogen, carbon dioxide is difficult to spot. But in other ways carbon dioxide is very different from hydrogen.

- **Carbon dioxide is heavier than air.**
- **Carbon dioxide does not burn.**

These two properties make the gas very good at putting out fires.

ⓐ **Why do these two properties make carbon dioxide good at putting out fires?**

Carbon dioxide is also the gas that gives fizzy drinks their fizz. Animals breathe out carbon dioxide.

A test for carbon dioxide

When we bubble carbon dioxide through a liquid called **limewater**, the limewater turns from clear to milky white.

Look at the picture. It shows a reaction between an acid and a carbonate. A gas is given off. The gas is bubbling through limewater. The limewater is turning milky white. This means that the gas must be carbon dioxide.

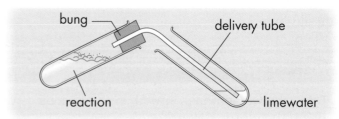

Carbon dioxide is so heavy that you could even pour it into the limewater.

ⓑ **Why can you pour carbon dioxide from one test tube to another?**

What is a carbonate?

Carbonates are very common chemicals.

Chalk, marble and baking powder are all carbonates.
They all react with acids to release carbon dioxide.

c **Why do you think the marble statue would be damaged by acid rain?**

Look at the picture. Acid is reacting with chalk.

d **How can you tell that a reaction is taking place?**

QUESTIONS

Copy these sentences and fill in the spaces using the words below:

>   burn   carbonates   carbon dioxide
>   limewater   milky

Carbon dioxide turns _____ a _____ colour.
It is released when acids react with _____ .
The gas _____ is heavier than air and does
not _____ .

KEY POINTS

- Carbon dioxide is invisible and does not smell.

- Carbon dioxide is heavier than air and does not burn.

- Acids react with carbonates.

- The reaction releases a gas called carbon dioxide.

What is burning?

Burning is a chemical reaction. We know this because during burning, things become changed for ever. Ashes never change back into paper or coal.

ⓐ **When we burn gas in a gas cooker, the flame never turns back into the gas. How do we know that this is a chemical reaction?**

Burning needs oxygen

Like hydrogen and carbon dioxide, **oxygen** is also an invisible gas. But its other properties are very different.

Oxygen helps things to burn. For anything to burn it needs three things: fuel, heat and oxygen.

ⓑ **Look at the picture of the fire triangle. Which three things are needed for burning to take place?**

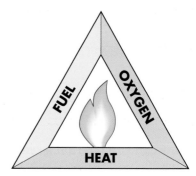

The **fire triangle**

A test for oxygen

Oxygen helps things to burn so much that it will relight a glowing splint of wood. This is the test that we use for oxygen.

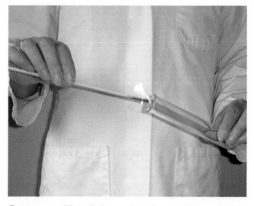

Oxygen will relight a glowing splint

Air contains oxygen

Air contains some oxygen. This is why things will burn in air.

Things burn much better in pure oxygen. They burn faster with a brighter, hotter flame.

c **Why do things burn slower in air than in pure oxygen?**

What is made during burning?

Whenever a substance burns in oxygen, an **oxide** is made. Some oxides are called dioxides.

If we burn magnesium in oxygen, we get magnesium oxide.

magnesium + oxygen → magnesium oxide

When carbon in coal burns, we get carbon dioxide.

d **What do you think is burned in oxygen to get sulphur dioxide?**

Magnesium burning in oxygen

QUESTIONS

Copy these sentences and fill in the spaces using the words below:

air   burning   carbon

faster   oxide   oxygen

_____ is a chemical reaction. In order to burn, we need fuel, heat and _____ . Oxygen is found in the _____ that we breathe. This is why things burn in air. When a substance burns it makes an _____ . It burns much _____ in pure oxygen. Carbon dioxide is made when _____ burns.

KEY POINTS

- Burning is a chemical reaction.
- Air contains oxygen.
- Oxygen helps things to burn.
- When a substance burns, we get an oxide or a dioxide.

Fuels

Fuels are substances that burn. They release heat energy that we can use.

Look at the pictures. They are all examples of different types of fuels.

Camping gas

Petrol

Bonfire

Jet fuel

Look at this picture of an electric fire. The electric fire is using electrical energy to make heat.

ⓐ Why is electricity not a fuel?

Fossil fuels

Fossil fuels are fuels that occur in nature. They have been formed like fossils. They have been in the ground for a long time. The three main fossil fuels are:

coal   oil   natural gas

They all contain carbon. When the carbon in these fuels burns, carbon dioxide is produced.

Electric fire

Types of fuel

Fuels can be divided into three types.

solid fuels   liquid fuels   gas fuels

ⓑ Look at the pictures at the top of the page. Write down one example of each type of fuel.

Burning natural gas

Natural gas is the gas we use in our homes. It is a chemical called **methane**. Methane is a very clean fuel. It produces less pollution than coal.

c **Give one reason why we should burn methane instead of coal.**

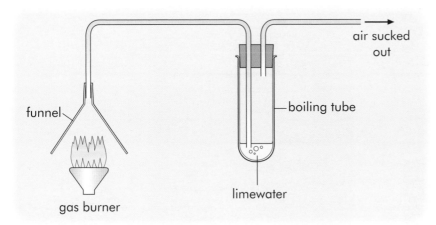

When methane burns it produces carbon dioxide. Look at the picture. It shows an experiment to prove that burning methane produces carbon dioxide.

d **What colour will the limewater turn as carbon dioxide bubbles through it?**

QUESTIONS

Copy these sentences and fill in the spaces using the words below:

> carbon   carbon dioxide   energy
>
> fossil   methane

Fuels release _____ when they burn. Coal, oil and gas are all examples of _____ fuels. All these fuels contain _____ . This means that when they burn they produce the gas _____.
Natural gas is a chemical called _____ .

KEY POINTS

- Fuels release heat energy when we burn them.

- Fossil fuels are found in the ground.

- Natural gas is a fossil fuel called methane.

- Carbon dioxide is produced when a fossil fuel burns.

Air and burning

How do we know that burning just uses part of the air
and not all of the air? We can show that this happens
by carrying out the following experiment.

A burning candle uses up oxygen

The water level rises

The burning candle floats on the surface of the water.
It burns and uses up part of the air in the jar. It then
goes out. The water level rises to replace the part of the
air that has been used up.

We know that the part of the air that is used up is
oxygen. We know this because oxygen reacts with
substances that are burning.

ⓐ **The water level rises up the jar by 20%. What
percentage of the air in the jar was oxygen?**

ⓑ **Why did the candle go out after a few seconds?**

What happens to the carbon dioxide?

We know that when fuels burn, they release carbon
dioxide. The carbon dioxide cannot be in the gas jar or
the water level would not have risen. The carbon
dioxide must have dissolved into the water.

ⓒ **Where did the carbon dioxide go from the
burning candle?**

Simple chemical reactions

How long will the candle burn?

The candle goes out when there is not enough oxygen left to keep the candle burning.

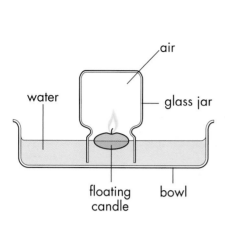

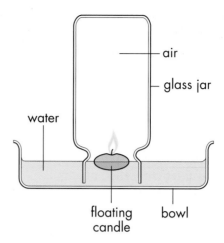

d Look at the picture. Which will burn for longer, the candle in the small jar or the candle in the large jar?

This is called making a prediction. You could test your prediction by carrying out an experiment to see how long each candle burns.

Some students carried out an experiment. They used six different sized containers. The table shows how long the candle burned in each of them.

e Draw a graph and plot the points from the table.

f Does the candle stay lit for longer in the 300 cm³ container or the 500 cm³ container?

Volume of container (cm³)	Time that the candle stays alight (seconds)
100	5
200	10
300	15
400	17
500	20
600	25

QUESTIONS

Copy these sentences and fill in the spaces using the words below:

> dissolves   oxygen   stop

20% of the air is a gas called _____ . Some of the carbon dioxide produced when things burn _____ in water. Things _____ burning when all of the oxygen has been used up.

KEY POINTS

- Air contains 20% oxygen.

- Carbon dioxide dissolves in water.

G Particle model of solids, liquids and gases

G1 HOW ARE THEORIES CREATED?

A bright idea?

People have been thinking about what things are made of for thousands of years. 2500 years ago, some clever men who lived in Greece had some ideas. One of them said that everything was made up of tiny particles called **atoms**.

Another man did not agree. He said everything was made of a mixture of earth, air, fire and water. We now know that the first man's idea was correct. But people believed the second man and everyone got it wrong for the next 2000 years.

It is not surprising that people believed the wrong idea. When they looked around them they could see earth, water and air. They thought that fire was released when things started to burn.

It was not until 300 years ago that someone realised the first man had been right after all. This someone was a scientist called John Dalton.

Solids, liquids and gases

All substances are a solid, or a liquid, or a gas.

Solids keep the same shape and size.

Liquids keep the same size, but can change their shape.

Gases can change their shape and their size.

ⓐ Look at the pictures. Decide whether each one is a solid, a liquid or a gas.

A rock

Sea water

Helium-filled balloons

A sandcastle

A book

A fizzy drink

ⓑ Write down one more solid, liquid and gas that you would find in your home.

QUESTIONS

Copy these sentences and fill in the spaces using the words below:

shape   size

Solids keep the same _____ and size. Liquids change their _____ but not their _____ . Gases change their _____ and their _____ .

KEY POINTS

- Solids keep the same size and shape.

- Liquids keep the same size, but change their shape.

- Gases change their shape and their size.

HOW DO SOLIDS, LIQUIDS AND GASES BEHAVE?

Solids, liquids and gases behave in some very strange ways. We are going to look at how they behave. Then we are going to try to explain it.

Some odd behaviour

When you try to squash a solid or a liquid, you can't.

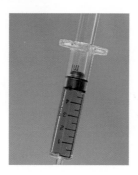

When you try to squash a gas, you can.

Solids usually get bigger when you heat them. When cold, the bar fits. When hot it does not fit any more because it has got bigger.

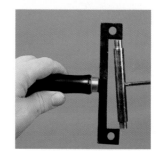

If you drop a crystal in water, it dissolves. The colour gradually spreads out.

A heavy weight is hanging from a wire. This makes the wire stretch. Eventually the wire will snap.

How can we explain all these things?

Particle model of solids, liquids and gases

Particles can explain what we see

Imagine that everything is made of tiny **particles**.
These students are using the idea of particles to explain
what they see.

Fergus

I think that we can squash a gas because the particles are further apart to start with.

I think that the metal bar expanded when hot because the particles got further apart.

Ravinder

I think the wire stretched because the particles slid past one another.

Pip

I think the colour spread out because the particles are moving.

Umesh

a How would you use the idea of particles to explain that some metals are heavier than others?

QUESTIONS

Copy these sentences and fill in the spaces using the words below:

> further   move   particles   squashed

Particles are _____ apart in a gas. This is why gases can be _____ . Things get bigger when heated because the _____ move further apart. The colour from the crystal spreads because the particles _____ .

KEY POINTS

- Particles can be used to explain how solids, liquids and gases behave.

Grouping solids, liquids and gases

Putting things into different groups is called **classifying**. Look at the picture. It shows lots of different substances.

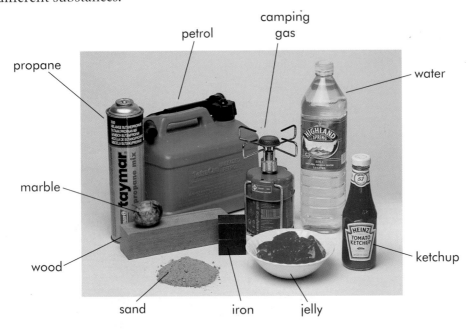

propane
petrol
camping gas
water
marble
wood
sand
iron
jelly
ketchup

ⓐ Put each substance in the picture into one of three groups: a solid, a liquid or a gas.

Some things just don't fit!

You probably found the task quite hard. Some things do not easily fit into one of the groups. Tomato ketchup does not change its size. It changes its shape but only very slowly. Is it a solid or a liquid?

To try and answer this question, look at the label from a tomato ketchup bottle.

ⓑ Look at the list of ingredients on the label. Make a list of all the ingredients.

ⓒ For each substance, write down whether it is a solid, a liquid or a gas.

TOMATO KETCHUP
We are very proud of Heinz Tomato Ketchup. One of the original Heinz '57 Varieties', our ketchup has stood for quality and authenticity for over 100 years. If you are not delighted with this ketchup simply write to us quoting the quality code on the bottle cap for a full refund. Your statutory rights are not affected.
INGREDIENTS: Tomatoes (126g per 100g Ketchup), Spirit Vinegar Glucose Syrup, Sugar, Salt, Spice and Herb Extracts, Spice, Garlic Powder.

NUTRITION INFORMATION		
TYPICAL VALUES	PER 100g	PER SERVING (10ml)

Mixtures

You probably spotted that this is a trick question. Tomato ketchup is not one substance. It is a **mixture** of different substances. Some are liquids and some are solids. This is why tomato ketchup behaves in such an odd way.

Most substances that are difficult to classify are mixtures. A **foam** is like this.

ⓓ **A foam is a mixture. It is a mixture of a liquid and something else. Is the 'something else' in a foam a solid, a liquid or a gas?**

A **gel** is also a mixture. It is a mixture of a solid and a liquid. This is why hair gel can be a liquid when we put it on our hair and a solid when we leave it there.

Look at the picture. Gels can be useful in all sorts of ways.

ⓔ **Can you think of any other gels that are not shown in the picture?**

QUESTIONS

Classify each of the following as a solid, a liquid, a gas or a mixture:

paper clip   water   jelly
steam   crazy foam   hair gel

KEY POINTS

- We can put substances into three groups: solids, liquids and gases. This is called classifying.

- Mixtures are more difficult to classify.

- Mixtures behave in different ways.

THE PARTICLE MODEL OF SOLIDS, LIQUIDS AND GASES

What is a particle?

Particles are very small 'bits' of something. Particles are so small we can hardly see them even with the most powerful microscope. Each particle has a fixed shape and size.

It is how the particles are arranged in a substance that decides whether it will be a solid, liquid or gas.

Using a model

It is hard to imagine things that we cannot see. Using a **model** makes it easier to understand particles.

We are going to use grains of sand as a model for the tiny particles we can't see.

Solid

When grains of sand are stuck together, they cannot move. We call this solid sandstone.

Liquid

When grains of sand are free to move about, they can flow like a liquid. The grains can move past one another.

Gas

When grains of sand are blown in a sandstorm, they behave like a gas. The grains are far apart and they are travelling in different directions.

The particle theory

The sand model helps us to imagine how particles behave.

In **solids** we can imagine millions of tiny particles. They are all close together and fixed in place.

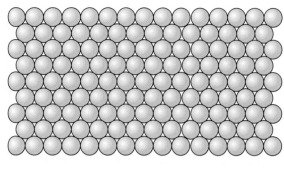

In **liquids** the particles are free to move past each other.

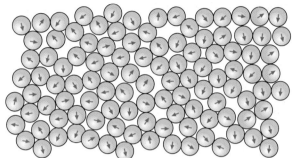

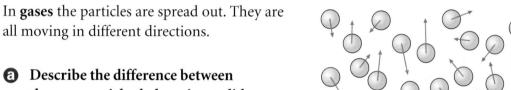

In **gases** the particles are spread out. They are all moving in different directions.

ⓐ Describe the difference between the way particles behave in a solid and in a liquid.

ⓑ Describe the difference between the way particles behave in a liquid and in a gas.

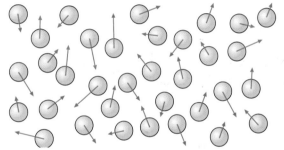

QUESTIONS

Copy these sentences and fill in the spaces using the words below:

apart   directions   fixed   model   move

Particles in a solid are close together and _____ . In a liquid, the particles are free to _____ . In a gas, the particles are far _____ and move in different _____ . We can use a _____ to help us understand how particles work.

KEY POINTS

● Particles are very small. They have a fixed shape and size.

● We can use a model to help us understand how particles behave.

● Particles are fixed in a solid, move in a liquid and spread out in a gas.

Explaining gas pressure

A 'big idea', such as the idea that all substances are made up of particles, is called a **theory**. If the particle theory is correct, it should also be able to explain why a gas causes **pressure**.

When we blow up a balloon, the pressure of the air that we blow into it pushes the walls of the balloon outwards. The more air we put into the balloon, the more pressure there is. The balloon gets bigger. It is the particles of air bumping into the sides of the balloon that keep it blown up.

Increasing pressure

Not all containers are like balloons. Some do not get bigger as we put more gas in them. Look at the picture of the two jars. One has more gas particles inside than the other.

ⓐ Which jar has more particles hitting its sides?

ⓑ Which jar has the higher gas pressure?

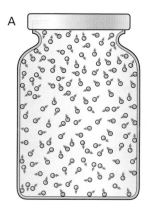
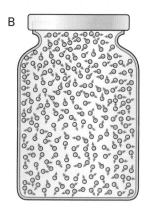

Decreasing pressure

Most empty cans are not really empty at all. They are full of air.

Look at the picture. The pump has removed all of the air from inside the can. The can collapsed inwards when the air was removed.

Was it sucked or was it pushed?

Some people might think the can collapsed because it was sucked inwards. Other people think that the can collapsed because the air particles on the outside of the can pushed the can inwards.

c **Which do you think is the correct reason? Try to explain your answer.**

Explaining diffusion

Diffusion happens when particles spread out. The smell of perfume spreads round a room. It spreads by diffusion as the perfume particles spread out.

Look at the two pictures of a beaker.

The beaker contains water. In the first picture some ink is placed at the bottom.

The second picture shows the beaker several hours later.

We can explain what happens using the particle theory. The particles of ink and the particles of water are moving about. This means they will mix and the colour will gradually spread out.

At start   After several hours

QUESTIONS

Copy these sentences and fill in the spaces using the words below:

  bump diffusion higher spread

Pressure is caused when particles _____ into the walls of their container. The greater the number of particles, the _____ the pressure.

Diffusion happens when particles _____ outwards. Perfume smell spreading around a room is an example of _____ .

KEY POINTS

- The particle theory can be used to explain gas pressure.

- The particle theory can be used to explain diffusion.

H Solutions

HOW CAN WE TELL WHEN A LIQUID IS A MIXTURE?

When substances dissolve

It is very difficult to tell whether a liquid has something dissolved in it. You cannot tell whether a cup of tea has sugar in it unless you taste it. Sometimes it is not possible to taste things.

ⓐ Look at the picture. One of the beakers contains pure water and the other has poison dissolved in the water. Can you tell which is which?

What soluble and insoluble mean

- **Soluble** means that it will dissolve.
- **Insoluble** means that it will not dissolve.

Sugar is soluble. Sand is not. If sand was soluble, it would dissolve in the sea and we would have no beaches left.

Solutions are mixtures

Solutions are mixtures, usually of a solid and a liquid. The solid dissolves so we cannot see it. But it is still there in the mixture.

ⓑ Make a list of mixtures that have a solid dissolved in a liquid.

How to separate these mixtures

If a solution is a mixture, we can separate it. One method is to heat the solution until the liquid **evaporates**. The solid will be left sitting there all by itself.

Many people think that tap water is a pure substance. But if you leave some in a shallow dish for a few days, the water will evaporate. The solids in the mixture are left behind in the dish.

c **Use the idea of particles to explain where the water has gone.**

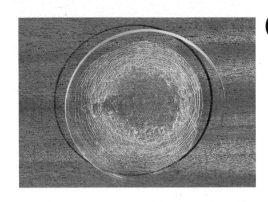

Why can't we separate solutions by filtering?

When something dissolves, the particles are spread through the water. The particles are so small that they go straight through a filter. This means that we cannot separate solutions by filtering them.

Look at the picture. Sand grains are big enough to be stopped by the filter. The sugar goes straight through.

Sand   Sugar

QUESTIONS

Copy these sentences and fill in the spaces using the words below:

    evaporating   filtering   mixture   not

It is _____ always possible to tell whether something is dissolved in water just by looking at it. A solution is a _____ of a solid and liquid. We can separate a solution by _____ the liquid. It is not possible to separate a solution by _____ .

KEY POINTS

- A solution is a mixture of a solid and a liquid.

- We can separate a solution by evaporating the liquid.

- Filtering will not separate the mixture in a solution.

Salt

Salt is a substance that can be dug out of the ground. It is called **rock salt**.

Look at the picture. It shows the inside of a large salt mine. Salt is mined like this in Cheshire.

In some countries, people get salt from sea water. They leave the sea water to evaporate. The salt is left behind and the people collect it. This is called **sea salt**.

Using salt

Many of us sprinkle salt on our chips and other food. Salt has lots of other uses. People use it to make plastic, paper and soap.

People also use salt to make chemicals for farming. We even use it in the dishwasher to help clean the plates.

ⓐ Can you think of any more uses for salt?

ⓑ Why do you think people only get salt from sea water in hot countries?

How to get pure salt from rock salt

Rock salt is pure salt with a few extra substances in it. We call these extra substances **impurities**. You can get pure salt from rock salt by:

1 Crushing the rock salt

First we crush the rock salt to break it up into small pieces.

2 Adding water

Then we add water. The salt dissolves in the water, but the impurities don't.

c Look at the picture. Why is the solution of rock salt brown?

3 Filtering

We then **filter** the solution to remove all the impurities.

d How do we get crystals of salt from the salt solution?

Is there a better way to get the salt?

Look at the three pictures on this page. Not all of the salt dissolves when you mix it with water. Some salt will be left in the filter paper.

e Charlie poured some more pure water through the filter paper. Explain why this water contained salt when it dripped into the beaker.

QUESTIONS

Copy these sentences and fill in the spaces using the words below:

>   evaporating   ground   impurities

We mine rock salt from the _____ . We separate sea salt by _____ sea water. Rock salt contains _____ that we remove to make it pure.

KEY POINTS

- Rock salt is salt mixed with impurities.

WHAT HAPPENS TO THE SOLUTE DURING DISSOLVING?

What is the solute?

The **solute** is what scientists call the substance that dissolves. When we put sugar into a cup of tea, the sugar is the solute.

The disappearing solute trick

Where does the sugar go when you stir it into a cup of tea? You only have to taste the tea to know that it is still there. But where has it gone?

One way to find out is to weigh the cup of tea before you add the sugar. Then weigh the sugar. Then weigh the cup of tea with the sugar in it.

ⓐ The cup of tea weighs 300 g. The sugar weighs 50 g. How much will the cup of tea weigh with the sugar added?

The cup of tea will weigh exactly 350 g. Some people don't believe this because they think the sugar has disappeared. But even though we cannot see it, the sugar is still there.

This is always true when we dissolve things:

● The total weight is always the weight of the liquid plus the weight of the solute.

Using the particle model

We can use the idea of particles to explain where the sugar has gone. We know that solids and liquids are made of tiny particles. When you put the sugar into the tea, the sugar breaks up into separate particles.

Each sugar particle becomes surrounded by water particles. The sugar particles are much too small to see. They seem to disappear, even though they are still there.

Why filtering won't work

When the solid sugar is added to the tea, it dissolves. If you try to separate the sugar from the tea by filtering it, it won't work. This is because the particles of sugar are very small.

Look at the picture. It shows a greatly magnified view of a piece of filter paper.

If you look carefully you will see that the paper is full of holes. The sugar particles would pass straight through these holes.

ⓑ Imagine some grit fell in your cup of tea. Why would it be possible to filter the grit out of the tea using the filter paper in the picture?

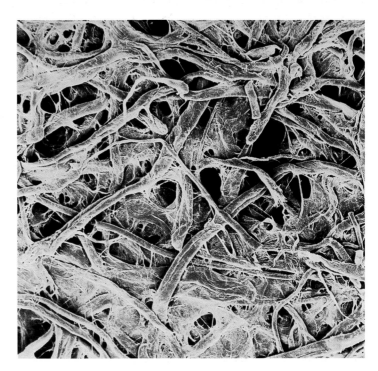

QUESTIONS

Copy these sentences and fill in the spaces using the words below:

disappear   liquid   same   separate   solute

A substance that dissolves in a liquid is called a _____ . It seems to _____ but in fact it is still there. The particles of the solid _____ and become surrounded by _____ particles.

If we weighed the liquid and the solute before mixing, they would weigh the _____ after they were mixed together.

KEY POINTS

- A substance that dissolves is called a solute.

- When a solid dissolves, the small particles separate.

- The particles are small enough to pass through filter paper.

What is a solvent?

A **solvent** is a liquid that a solute dissolves in. If the sugar is the solute, then the water is the solvent.

Water is a very good solvent. Stain removers contain other solvents that are good for removing stains.

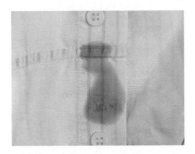 

Getting the solvent back

Sometimes we need to get the solvent back from a solution. If you had sea water but no fresh water, you would want to get the solvent, the pure water, back. Hopefully, before you died of thirst.

If you need very pure water, it is no good using tap water. That has lots of things dissolved in it. You need to get the solvent, the pure water, out of the mixture.

Earlier in this unit we looked at a picture of what is left behind when tap water evaporates.

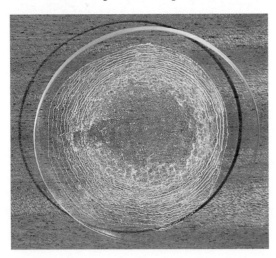

Distillation

Distillation is a way of getting the solvent back.
It separates the solvent from the mixture.

1 Heating the mixture

The first step is to heat the mixture. This makes the
solvent evaporate. The solute, the substance that was
dissolved, is left behind.

ⓐ What does the word evaporate mean?

2 Cooling the solvent

Cooling the solvent turns it back into a liquid.
We say the solvent **condenses**.

ⓑ Can you think of anywhere in your home
where something condenses?

ⓒ What do we call water vapour that turns
back into a liquid on a cold window?

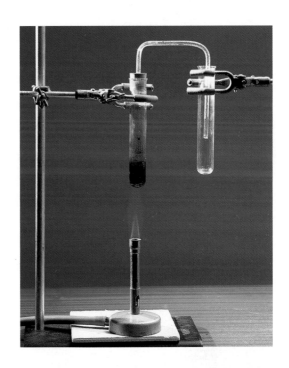

Distilling ink

We can show how distillation works by using
blue ink. Blue ink is a mixture of dye dissolved
in water.

If we heat the ink, the water evaporates. The
tube collects the steam and cools it. The steam
then turns back into clear water.

QUESTIONS

Copy these sentences and fill in the spaces
using the words below:

   condensing   distillation   heating   solvent

A solute dissolves in a _____ . We can get
the solvent back from the mixture by _____ .

Distillation means _____ the mixture and
then _____ the solvent back to a liquid.

KEY POINTS

● A solvent is a liquid that a
solute dissolves in.

● The solvent can be separated
from the solution by
distillation.

● Distillation can be used to
separate pure drinking water
from sea water.

What is chromatography?

It is sometimes difficult to separate a mixture by distillation. Perhaps you have a mixture of two solids dissolved in a solution. If you evaporate the solvent, they will still be mixed.

ⓐ **Why would distillation not be a good method to separate out two solutes from a mixture?**

Chromatography can be used to separate many different kinds of mixture.

How chromatography works

Most inks are a mixture of different coloured dyes in a liquid. We can separate these different coloured dyes by using chromatography.

Put a drop of black ink in the centre of the filter paper. Cut a wick, or tongue, of paper as shown in the picture.

Put the paper on top of a beaker of water with the wick just dipping into the water.

The water soaks up the wick and spreads outwards.

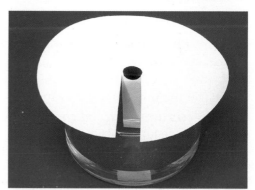

The different dyes spread out with the water at different speeds.

Some dyes spread as fast as the water. Others spread more slowly and are left behind.

Soon we can see the different coloured dyes appearing. We call this a **chromatogram** or 'coloured picture'.

ⓑ **What other colour is present in the black ink?**

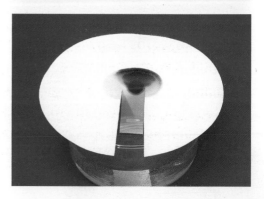

 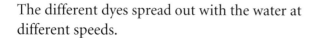

How we use chromatography

We can use chromatography to find out what is in a solution. Food scientists use it to find out what is in food. The police use it to match paint taken from crime scenes. Drug testers use it to see if athletes have taken banned drugs.

Look at the picture. It shows the dyes found in a yellow Smartie, along with some other yellow food colourings.

Look at the picture below of a chromatogram. It shows four different dyes called A, B, C and D. It also shows the dyes found in a different coloured Smartie, called substance X.

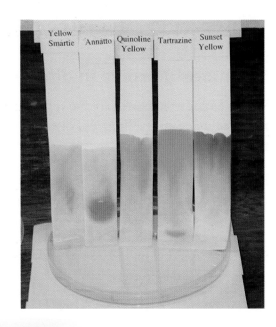

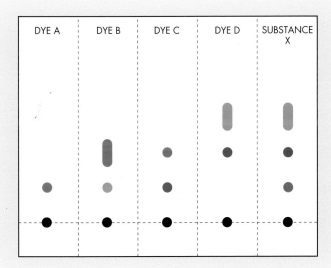

Ⓒ **Which of the dyes A, B, C and D are used to make the Smartie called substance X?**

QUESTIONS

Copy these sentences and fill in the spaces using the words below:

  coloured   chromatography   substances

We can separate different coloured dyes using _____ . We can use chromatography to find out what _____ are in a mixture.
Chromatogram means _____ picture.

KEY POINTS

- Chromatography can be used to separate mixtures.

Do things dissolve in different solvents?

Some solutes will dissolve in one solvent, but not in others. Some solutes will dissolve in many different solvents.

For example, beaker **A** shows that sulphur will not dissolve in water. But sulphur will dissolve in alcohol, as shown in beaker **B**.

Salt will dissolve in both water and alcohol.

A   B

How much can dissolve?

Sometimes lots of a solute will dissolve in a solvent. With other solutes, only a little bit dissolves in the solvent.

We know that salt dissolves in water. But twice as much potassium bromide will dissolve in the same amount of water. We say that potassium bromide is very soluble.

What is a saturated solution?

A **saturated solution** is one that contains so much solute, no more will dissolve in it.

You can tell when a solution is saturated. If you add any more solute, it just falls to the bottom. It will not dissolve no matter how long you stir it.

The **solubility** of a substance is how much solute will dissolve in 100 cm³ of solvent.

Does temperature make a difference?

Does it dissolve more quickly?

You know that sugar dissolves faster in a hot cup of tea than a cold one. Temperature does make a difference. Usually, the hotter the solvent is, the quicker the solute will dissolve.

Will more solute dissolve?

The temperature also affects how much will dissolve. Usually, the hotter the solvent is, the more solute will dissolve.

Maria carried out an experiment to see how much copper sulphate would dissolve in water. She did the experiment at five different temperatures.

Look at her table of results.

Temperature of solvent (°C)	Amount of copper sulphate that can dissolve in 100 cm³ of water (g)
0	14
20	21
40	29
60	40
80	55

ⓐ How much copper sulphate dissolved at 20 °C?

ⓑ How much copper sulphate dissolved at 60 °C?

Maria allowed the test tube of copper sulphate solution at 80 °C to cool down.

Look at the pictures of the copper sulphate solution cooling down. As the solution cools, less copper sulphate can dissolve in the water, so crystals of copper sulphate start to form.

ⓒ Why are crystals of copper sulphate forming?

Cooling the solution   Crystals forming

QUESTIONS

Copy these sentences and fill in the spaces using the words below:

saturated   soluble   solubility   temperature

When no more solute can dissolve in a solvent, the solution is _____ .

Scientists call how much solute can dissolve the _____ . Some substances are more _____ than others. The _____ will affect how much solute can dissolve.

KEY POINTS

● A solution in which no more solute can dissolve is called saturated.

● Temperature affects how much and how quickly a solute will dissolve in a solvent.

I Energy resources

I1 WHY ARE FUELS USEFUL?

When fuels burn

When fuels burn, they give us light and heat.
Light and heat are useful forms of energy.

Gas, oil and coal are examples of fuels.

a What other things can we burn as fuel?

What is energy?

Energy makes things happen.

A car needs energy to make it move.
The energy comes from the fuel.

heat from engine

petrol is fuel

movement energy

What is a fuel?

A **fuel** is just a store of energy. When we burn it, the stored energy is turned into light and heat. Light and heat are different kinds of energy.

Petrol is the fuel burned in cars. It releases heat energy. The car uses this heat energy to move.

In many power stations, the fuel is gas or coal. The power station burns the fuel and turns the stored energy into electricity.

Humans eat food for fuel. We use the energy in our food to run, walk and talk. In fact we get the energy for everything we do from our food.

We get hot when we run fast, because we burn more fuel to provide the extra energy for running.

runner gets hot

energy from food

Other sources of energy

It is not just fuel that provides us with energy. We can also get energy from the wind, from flowing water or from the Sun. The energy from the Sun can burn us if we stay out in the sunshine for too long.

ⓑ These windmills are making electricity. Where do you think they get their energy from?

Measuring heat energy

When you give a substance a lot of heat energy, it gets hotter. We call how hot something is its **temperature**. We can measure temperature with a **thermometer**.

How to read a thermometer

The thermometers we use in school measure temperature in degrees Celsius or °C. Sometimes each line on the scale equals 1 °C. But sometimes each line on the scale may equal 2 °C or even $\frac{1}{2}$ °C.

It is important to look carefully and work out what each line on the scale means.

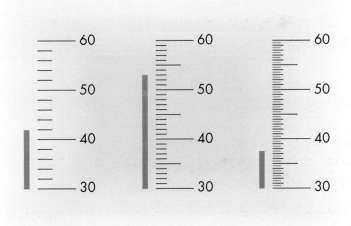

A   B   C

ⓒ Look at the three thermometer scales. Write down the reading for each thermometer.

QUESTIONS

Copy these sentences and fill in the spaces using the words below:

electricity   energy   fuel   light

When a _____ burns, heat and _____ are released. Heat and light are examples of _____ . Another kind of energy is _____ .

Which fuel is best?

Some fuels give us more heat than others. We can compare fuels by seeing how much they will heat up a beaker of water. To keep it a fair test, we need to use the same amount of water each time.

ⓐ Why is it important that we use the same amount of water each time?

Using a Bunsen burner safely

A Bunsen burner burns gas, the same gas that people use in kitchens for cooking. Gas can be dangerous so it is important to know how to use a Bunsen burner safely.

- Always wear goggles.
- Always tie your hair back and wear a lab coat.
- Check the rubber tube is not damaged.
- Make sure the beaker won't fall over.
- Use a blue flame to heat the water.
- Change to a yellow flame when you are not using the Bunsen burner. The yellow makes the flame easy to see so you don't forget the burner is on.

ⓑ Why should you always leave the Bunsen burner with a yellow flame when you are not using it?

Heating water

Look at the picture. We can use this apparatus to find out how quickly a Bunsen burner heats water.

Anna set up the apparatus. She measured the temperature of the water at the start, so she could work out how much the water warmed up.

She then measured the temperature of the water every minute, for 5 minutes.

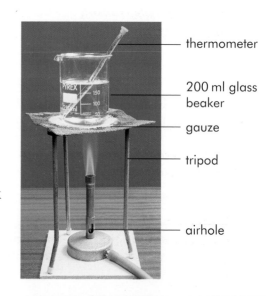

thermometer

200 ml glass beaker

gauze

tripod

airhole

Anna's results are shown in the table.

c What was the temperature of the water at the start of the experiment?

d What was the temperature after 5 minutes?

Time (mins)	Temperature (°C)
0	10
1	24
2	35
3	45
4	56
5	67

Burning gas

Comparing fuels

Anna repeated the experiment. But this time she used some solid camping fuel instead of gas and a Bunsen burner.

Look at the table. These are her results using solid camping fuel.

e Why did Anna take the temperature of the water before she started?

f What was the temperature at the start of the experiment?

g What was the temperature after 5 minutes?

h Look at the results for burning gas and solid camping fuel. Which heated the water up most over 5 minutes?

i Why would gas from a gas pipe not be a good choice of fuel if you were camping?

Time (mins)	Temperature (°C)
0	18
1	19
2	20
3	21
4	22
5	23

Burning solid camping fuel

QUESTIONS

1 Explain how to use a Bunsen burner safely.

2 Copy these sentences and fill in the spaces using the words below:

energy   heat

Some fuels give out more heat _____ than others. We can compare how much _____ _____ is given out by different kinds of fuel.

KEY POINTS

- Some fuels give out more heat energy than others.

- We can compare the heat energy from different fuels.

- There may be other reasons for choosing a type of fuel, apart from the heat energy it produces.

I3 WHAT ARE FOSSIL FUELS?

What is a fossil fuel?

A fossil is the remains of an animal or plant that died millions of years ago. **Fossil fuels** are made from the fossil bodies of these animals and plants.

Fossil fuels take millions of years to make. When we have used them all up, there will be no more left, unless of course we want to wait for another few million years. As we cannot make more fossil fuels, we call these fuels **non-renewable**.

ⓐ Why are fossil fuels called non-renewable?

Types of fossil fuel

Coal

Coal is made from plants that lived 300 million years ago. There were no humans around then. When the trees died they fell into swamps. They became squashed and gradually turned into coal.

Crude oil

Crude oil is a black sticky liquid found deep underground. Millions of years ago, tiny sea creatures died and fell to the bottom of the sea. They became trapped under mud and gradually turned into oil.

Gas

Gas was formed at the same time as crude oil, and in the same way.

ⓑ Why is wood not a fossil fuel?

Using fossil fuels

Humans have been on the Earth for only 2 million years. Because fossil fuels are so hard to get out of the ground, we have only started to use a lot of them in the last 100 years or so.

Coal was the first fossil fuel people used. It is dirty and makes a lot of smoke and ash. Some countries are now running out of their coal.

Oil and gas are much cleaner and make less ash and smoke. Oil can be used to make petrol and plastics.

A coal-fired power station used to generate electricity.

c **Why do people prefer to use oil and gas as fuel rather than coal?**

Using fuels in the future

One day we will run out of all of our fossil fuels. Until then we have two choices. The first choice is to use less fossil fuels so that they last longer. The second choice is to find some other source of energy.

d **Most electricity is made from burning fossil fuel. Make a list of all the things you use in a day that use electricity.**

QUESTIONS

Think about your day again. Make a list of ways that you could use less electricity. Switching lights off in empty rooms is one example.

KEY POINTS

- Fossil fuels are made from the remains of animals and plants that lived hundreds of millions of years ago.

- The three most important fossil fuels are coal, oil and gas.

WHAT ARE RENEWABLE ENERGY RESOURCES?

What does renewable mean?

Renewable energy resources are sources of energy that do not get smaller when we use them. For example, using the Sun's energy does not change the amount of energy that arrives from the Sun. Unlike coal, oil and gas, the Sun's energy does not get used up.

Some renewable energy resources

1 Energy from water

We can use energy from fast-flowing water to make electricity. This is called **hydroelectricity**.

2 Energy from the Earth

Inside the Earth it is very hot. This can heat water just below the ground. We can use this hot water to make electricity. This is called **geothermal** energy.

3 Energy from waves

We can use the energy in waves to make electricity.

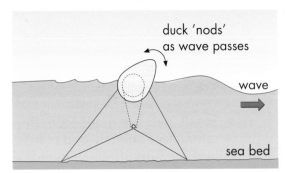

duck 'nods' as wave passes

wave

sea bed

4 Energy from wind

We can use energy from the wind to turn giant windmills. These produce electricity.

5 Energy from plants

We can grow plants for fuel. Some new power stations use wood as fuel. The wood quickly grows again ready to be cut down again.

6 Energy direct from the Sun

Energy from the Sun is called **solar energy**. **Solar panels** use solar energy to heat water. We can use this hot water in our homes.

The problem with solar energy is that it is not there at night, when it gets dark.

a What is a renewable energy resource?

b Write down three examples of renewable energy resources.

c Why do solar panels work better in sunny countries than in countries with less sunshine?

QUESTIONS

Copy these sentences and fill in the spaces using the words below:

geothermal   night   renewable   sunlight

Wind and waves are examples of _____ energy resources. Other examples are _____ and _____ energy. Solar panels do not work at _____ .

KEY POINTS

- Renewable energy resources do not get smaller when we use them.

HOW DO LIVING THINGS USE ENERGY?

Where do we get our energy from?

Humans need energy for movement and growth. Even standing still uses energy. When you sleep your heart keeps pumping and your lungs keep breathing. All of this needs energy.

Humans get their energy from food

It is important to eat the right type and the right amount of food. If you eat too little, your body won't work properly. If you eat too much, you won't use up all the energy and it will be turned into fat. You need some fat stored in your body but being too fat is not healthy. Neither is being too thin.

Releasing energy from food

We get energy from fuels by burning them. Your body gets energy from food in a very similar way. The food is combined with oxygen to release the energy.

We measure energy in **joules**. A joule is a very small amount of energy. If you pick up an apple that has dropped on the floor, you use 1 joule of energy.

Which foods store the most energy?

We can find out which foods store the most energy in the following experiment.

- Put 10 cm³ of water into a boiling tube.
- Measure the temperature of the water.
- Place some food below the water.
- Set fire to the food.
- Allow the flame to heat the water.
- When the flame goes out, measure the temperature of the water again.
- Work out the rise in water temperature.

ⓐ Does all of the energy in the burning food get transferred to the water?

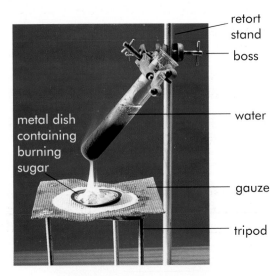

retort stand

boss

water

metal dish containing burning sugar

gauze

tripod

Food labels tell us how much energy the food contains.

Look at the picture. It shows how much energy there is in a bag of chocolates. The energy is given in kilojoules (kJ). One kilojoule is equal to 1000 joules.

A famous scientist called John Tyndall worked out that a ham sandwich contained enough energy to lift him to the top of a mountain. He then climbed the mountain with just one sandwich and got very hungry. He forgot that we also need energy to keep us warm and keep our heart pumping.

Ingredients: milk, sugar, cocoa mass, cocoa butter, vegetable fat, emulsifier: E442, flavourings.

Nutrition Information		Per Bag	Per 100 g
Energy	kJ	900	2195
	kcal	215	525
Protein	g	3.2	7.8
Carbohydrate	g	23.3	56.8
Fat	g	12.1	29.4

MILK SOLIDS 20% MINIMUM, COCOA SOLIDS 20% MINIMUM.

b **Why does a mountaineer have to eat more than one ham sandwich to climb a mountain?**

QUESTIONS

1 Why does your body use energy even when you are asleep?

2 Why does an active teenager use more energy than an older person?

3 Copy these sentences and fill in the spaces using the words below:

       energy   food   joules

Humans get their energy from _____ . Different foods contain different amounts of _____ . Energy is measured in units called _____ .

KEY POINTS

- We get our energy from food.
- Energy is measured in units called joules.
- 1000 joules is one kilojoule.

16 USING ENERGY

Where does the energy in food come from?

We have seen that food is full of stored energy. But where does this energy come from? The answer is that the energy comes from the Sun.

Plants make their food using energy from sunshine. The plants become a store for sunshine energy. When an animal eats the plant, the energy passes to the animal.

We call this passing on of energy a **food chain**.

Look at the food chain in the pictures.

The grass traps energy from the Sun. The cow gets the energy when it eats the grass. The cow passes the energy to us when we drink the cow's milk.

Grass   →   Cow   →   Human

ⓐ **Why could we say that we live on sunshine?**

ⓑ **Copy and complete the following food chain:**
grass → _____ → fox

The arrows show the way the energy flows in a food chain.

Why does most of our energy come from the Sun?

1 Fossil fuels like coal, oil and gas were made millions of years ago. They got their energy from sunshine millions of years ago.
2 Renewable fuels such as wood get their energy from sunshine.
3 Other renewable sources of energy like wind and waves are caused by the Sun affecting the Earth's weather.

It seems that almost all of our energy comes from the Sun.

How can we use energy well?

More people live on Earth now than ever before. We use more energy now than ever before.

When we burn fossil fuels, gases are given out, including carbon dioxide. Scientists think that carbon dioxide is causing the Earth to warm up. This will change weather patterns and cause flooding as the ice melts at the North and South Poles.

Renewable energy sources will not run out and they produce far less pollution than fossil fuels. But the wind does not always blow and the Sun does not always shine. It is much more difficult to get all the energy we need from renewable sources.

Look at the four students discussing the energy problem.

c **Copy out what each person is saying. Add why you agree or disagree with each one.**

We should use more solar power – the Sun's energy is everywhere.

Why carry on using up fossil fuels when we've got the wind and waves?

Amy

We could all use cars running on electricity – they're slower but cleaner.

Gopal

The rich countries use far more of the earth's resources than the poor ones – they should be the ones cutting back.

Raji

Jill

QUESTIONS

Copy these sentences and fill in the spaces using the words below:

chain   Sun

Most of our energy comes from the _____ .
We can show how the energy is passed from one living thing to another in a food _____ .

KEY POINTS

- Nearly all our energy comes from the Sun.

J Electrical circuits

J1 HOW DO ELECTRICAL CIRCUITS WORK?

What is current?

Think of blood flowing around your body. It flows through your blood vessels. Electricity flows through wires in a similar kind of way. Instead of flowing through blood vessels, electricity flows through **conductors**.

In your body, the blood flows from your heart, round your body and then back to your heart. We call this a **circuit**. Electricity also flows round a circuit.

Look at the picture. Most people would call this a battery. In fact it should really be called a **cell**.

The electricity goes from one end of the cell, through the wire and then back to the other end of the cell. Electricity flowing round a circuit is called **electric current**.

The cell pushes the electric current around the circuit.

ⓐ **What pushes electric current around the circuit?**

For a bulb to light in an electrical circuit, the circuit has to be complete. If the circuit is broken, the bulb will not light up.

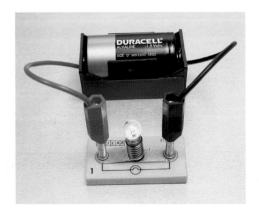

ⓑ Look at the pictures of circuits. Only one of them will work. Which one?

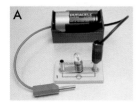 A

 B

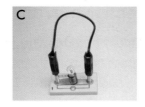 C

 D

How do we draw circuit diagrams?

We often want to draw electrical circuits. To make them easier to draw, we use **symbols**. Look at the table. It shows you the symbol for each part of a circuit.

Symbol	—	⊣⊢	⚬╱⚬	•—•	⊗
Part name	Wire	Cell	Open switch	Closed switch	Bulb

Look at the picture below. It shows a circuit with a bulb, a battery and a switch. The **circuit diagram** is next to it. The switch is open so the bulb is not lit.

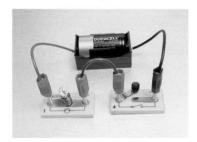

=

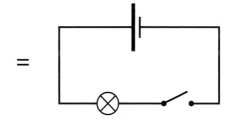

ⓒ Draw a circuit diagram for the picture opposite. If you look carefully you will see that the bulb is lit so you know which type of switch you should draw.

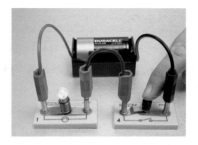

KEY POINTS

- Electric current flows round a circuit.
- The part we usually call a battery is called a cell.
- We can draw circuits using circuit diagrams.

QUESTIONS

1 Draw the symbols for a bulb, a cell and a switch.

2 How does a switch turn a bulb on and off?

WHAT HAPPENS IN A CIRCUIT?

What happens to electric current as it flows round the circuit?

The answer is – not a lot! Think of blood flowing round your body. Your heart pushes it round. All the blood that leaves the heart gets back to it a little later. The blood does not get used up.

In the same way, the cell pushes the current around the circuit. The current does not get used up.

How is current measured?

Think of water flowing along a river. The current in a circuit is like the amount of water flowing in the river. After heavy rain there is more water flowing. After a dry spell there is very little water flowing.

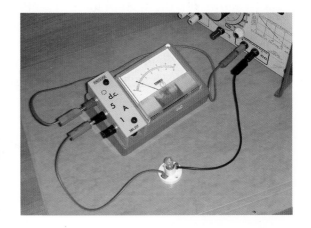

The size of the current can change too. We use an **ammeter** to measure the current flowing through a circuit. The picture shows an ammeter.

We measure electric current in units called **amps**.

Increasing current flow

A cell pushes electric current around a circuit. If we use two cells we get twice the push and more current will flow. Using two cells is like using a more powerful pump.

One cell = normal brightness of bulb

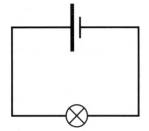

Two cells = very bright bulb

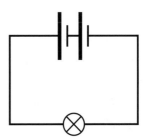

ⓐ **What would happen to the brightness of the bulb if we used three cells?**

Reducing the current flow

Twists and turns in blood vessels make it more difficult for the blood to flow in your body. The flow slows down because there is more resistance.

In the same way, in electrical circuits, bulbs resist the flow of electricity. The more bulbs, the lower the current. This is why when two bulbs are in the circuit, each bulb is much dimmer than if there was only one.

One bulb = normal brightness

Two bulbs = very dim

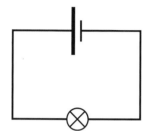
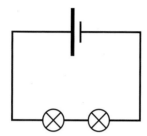

ⓑ What would happen to the brightness of the bulbs if we used three bulbs?

What is resistance?

Resistance is how difficult it is for current to flow through something. Plastic has so much resistance that electric current does not flow through it at all. Things that do not allow electricity to flow through them are called **insulators**. Plastic is an insulator.

QUESTIONS

Copy these sentences and fill in the spaces using the words below:

   brighter   amps   dimmer

Electric current is measured in _____ .
More cells will make the bulb glow _____ .
More bulbs will make the bulbs glow _____ .

KEY POINTS

- Electric current is measured in amps.

- More cells increase the flow of current.

- More bulbs increase the resistance in the circuit.

FAULT FINDING

What is a fault?

A fault is something that stops an electrical circuit from working. If your torch does not work it is because there is a fault in the circuit.

Look at the picture. The torch will not work because there are several faults in the circuit.

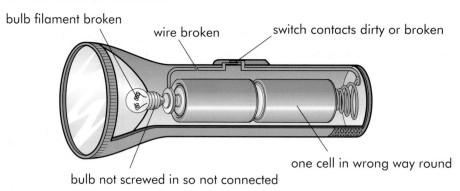

bulb filament broken

wire broken

switch contacts dirty or broken

one cell in wrong way round

bulb not screwed in so not connected

Finding a fault

There are two ways to find a fault. The first way is to replace each part of the circuit until it works again. This only works if there is one fault. If the bulb does not work we could replace it with a new one. But it will still not work if a wire is broken too.

ⓐ Why will the circuit not work if there are two faults?

The second way of finding a fault is to test each part of the circuit to see if it is working properly.

How do we test each part of the circuit?

The best way to test something is to put it in a circuit that you know is working.

Look at the picture. The bulb is lit, so the circuit is working. We can then test the bulb lying on its side by:

- unscrewing the lit bulb
- screwing the other bulb into the bulb holder
- checking to see if it lights
- if it does not light it must be faulty.

We can check other parts of the circuit, like the cell, in the same way.

ⓑ How could we check the cell to see if it is working?

What is a short circuit?

A **short circuit** happens when a wire is connected so that the current can flow without going through one part of the circuit. There is a short cut for the electric current. This is simpler than it sounds.

In this circuit, the current can flow round the short circuit and miss out the switch. The switch will not be able to turn the bulb off.

Look at pictures **A** and **B**. Neither circuit works properly.

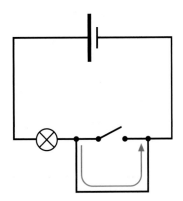

ⓒ In each of circuits A and B, which part will the current miss out?

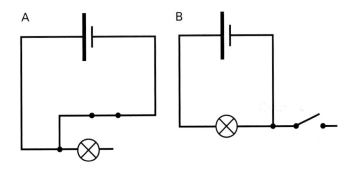

QUESTIONS

Copy these sentences and fill in the spaces using the words below:

circuit   fault   short

A _____ often stops electric current flowing in a circuit. We can find the fault by testing each part of the _____ . If there is a _____ circuit, the current can miss out part of the circuit.

KEY POINTS

● A fault often stops the electric current flowing around a circuit.

● We can find the fault by testing each part of the circuit.

● A short circuit allows the electric current to take a short cut and miss out part of the circuit.

CELLS, BATTERIES AND ELECTRIC CURRENTS

What is a cell?

A cell contains chemicals that give us a source of energy. The cell's job is to push electric current around the circuit.

We can measure how hard the cell pushes in units called **volts**. The cell in the picture pushes with 1.5 volts.

What is a battery?

A **battery** is two or more cells joined together. The torch on page 112 has a battery with two cells. It is important that the two cells are the right way round. If they were the wrong way round they would push in opposite directions and not much would happen. They both need to push the same way.

ⓐ **Why will the torch not work if the cells are facing in opposite directions?**

We call one end of the cell 'positive' and the other end 'negative'.

What does a battery push?

A single cell, or a battery with more than one cell, pushes electric current around the circuit. The electric current is made up of tiny moving particles called **electrons**. The cell pushes the electrons around the circuit.

It is easier to understand what is happening if we use a **model**. Look at the picture.

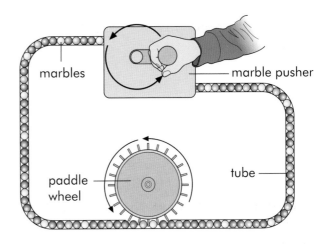

The tube is full of marbles. The marbles move round the circuit like electrons. Someone turns the handle to push the marbles round the circuit, just like the cell pushes electrons round the circuit.

As the marbles go past the paddle wheel they make the wheel turn. The paddle wheel turning is like the bulb lighting in the circuits we looked at before. The paddle wheel represents a bulb.

ⓑ What does each marble represent in the circuit?

ⓒ What does the person turning the handle represent in the circuit?

QUESTIONS

Copy these sentences and fill in the spaces using the words below:

cells   volts   electrons

A battery is two or more _____ joined together. It pushes _____ around the circuit. The amount a cell pushes is measured in _____ .

KEY POINTS

- A battery is two or more cells joined together.

- A cell pushes electric current or electrons around a circuit.

- The amount a cell pushes can be measured in volts.

PARALLEL CIRCUITS

What happens when the circuit is not simple?

The circuits we have met so far have been **simple circuits**. This is because the electricity can only go round the circuit by one path.

The top picture shows a simple circuit.

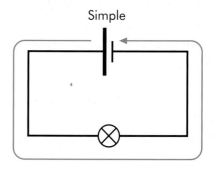
Simple

In some circuits, there is more than one path that the electric current can take. These are called **parallel circuits**.

The bottom picture shows a parallel circuit.

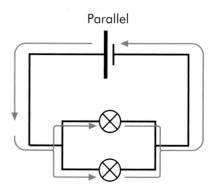
Parallel

Using a model to understand parallel circuits

ⓐ How bright do you think the bulbs will be in a parallel circuit?

Most people think that in a parallel circuit, the bulbs will be half as bright because they are sharing the electric current. In fact both bulbs are just as bright as the bulb in the simple circuit.

When the second bulb is in parallel with the first bulb, the current has two paths to follow. This makes it easier for the electric current to flow back to the cell. There is less resistance in the circuit. This means more current can flow.

Look at the models of a simple circuit and a parallel circuit.

The thin pipe is like a bulb. In the second picture we have added a second thin pipe. You can see that the same amount of water always flows through each of the thin pipes.

In the second picture the total flow is bigger. This is because the water can now flow though *both* thin pipes. It is the same with electric current. Adding another bulb in parallel lets the current flow through *both* bulbs.

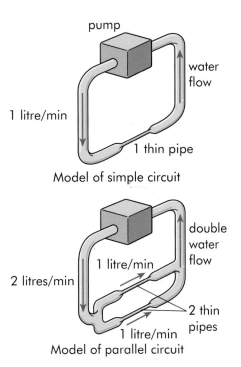

pump

water flow

1 litre/min

1 thin pipe

Model of simple circuit

double water flow

1 litre/min

2 litres/min

2 thin pipes

1 litre/min

Model of parallel circuit

Do models always work?

Models are very useful to explain how things work. But the problem with using a model is that it is never perfect.

In our model using water pipes, when a pipe breaks, water leaks out.

b Do you think electricity leaks out when a wire breaks?

QUESTIONS

Copy these sentences and fill in the spaces using the words below:

model   parallel   simple

A _____ circuit has only one way around a circuit. A _____ circuit has more than one way around the circuit. We can use a _____ to help us understand how a circuit works. But sometimes models do not work.

KEY POINTS

- Circuits that have more than one path are called parallel circuits.

- Bulbs are bright in a parallel circuit because there is less resistance in the circuit.

- Models do not always work.

What kind of circuit do we use at home?

Electricity in the home also flows in circuits.
Most houses use a type of circuit called a **ring main**.
The picture shows a diagram of a ring main.
It is really the same as a parallel circuit.

The big advantage of a ring main is that all the lights
can be switched on or off separately from each
other. When one bulb does not work, all the others
keep on working.

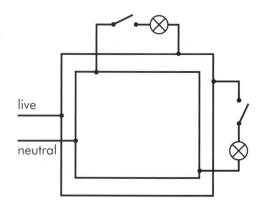

Electricity at home can be dangerous

One reason why electricity in the home can be
dangerous is that it is at a high voltage. This gives it a
much bigger push. Most homes use electricity at
230 volts. This is much higher than the 1.5 volt cells
that you use in a torch.

How do fuses work?

A **fuse** is a safety device. If the current gets too high,
the fuse stops current flowing. Fuses are a good idea
for three reasons:

- too high a current may damage parts of the circuit.
  A fuse is a lot cheaper than buying a new TV set.
- high currents make wires hot, which can cause fires.
  A fuse can stop a house burning down and save
  lives.
- a fuse stops the current flowing if there is a fault.
  This can help stop you getting an electric shock.

A fuse is just a thin piece of wire. If too much current flows through the wire, it gets very hot and melts. This breaks the circuit and the current stops flowing.

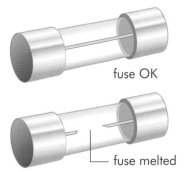

fuse OK

fuse melted

ⓐ Look at the picture of the fuses. Which fuse would you use to replace an old broken one?

Why is electricity dangerous?

Your heart gets small electric currents to make it work.

Some people have a faulty heart. A doctor might give them a pacemaker. The picture shows a pacemaker. It goes underneath the skin in the chest. It keeps the heart beating by giving it small electric shocks.

ⓑ Why would a pacemaker need a battery that lasts a long time?

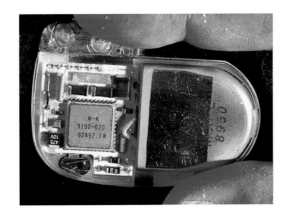

The current that flows through your body if you get an electric shock from mains electricity is thousands of times bigger than the current from the pacemaker. It is so powerful it can stop the heart beating altogether.

We should be very careful when we use electricity in the home.

KEY POINTS

- The kind of electrical circuit we use in our home is called a ring main.

- Fuses work by breaking the circuit if the current is too high.

- Electricity can be dangerous. It can stop your heart beating.

QUESTIONS

Copy these sentences and fill in the spaces using the words below:

            break   melt   ring

The electrical circuit we use in our homes is called a _____ main. If the current is too high, a fuse will _____ and _____ the circuit.

K Forces and their effects

What are forces?

Forces move things, or stop them moving. A force can also change the shape of an object or move it in a different direction.

Weight and friction are forces

Weight is the force that keeps us on the ground, or pulls us downwards. When you pick something up off the floor you are lifting it against a force. This force is the object's weight, which pulls it downwards.

Friction is the force you feel when you rub two surfaces against one another. A lot of friction makes it hard to move the surfaces against each other. The rougher the surfaces are, the more friction there is.

It is easier to push ice than wood.

ⓐ **Look at the picture. Which do you think has the rougher surface, ice or wood?**

ⓑ **Why is it easier to slide across ice than across wood?**

Friction can be useful

Shoelaces are rough. That is why there is a lot of friction and the knot does not come undone easily.

ⓒ **What would happen if the shoelaces were made of smooth plastic?**

Measuring forces

We can measure weight using a spring balance.
It is sometimes called a force meter.

Weighing with a force meter.

We can also use a force meter for measuring friction. We take the reading just as the object starts to move.

Weight and friction are forces and are measured in **newtons** (N).

Measuring friction using a force meter.

What is the difference between mass and weight?

Mass is the amount of 'stuff' an object has in it. An object like a cannon ball contains more 'stuff' than a ball of the same size made of cotton wool. The cannon ball has more mass.

Mass is measured in **kilograms** (kg).

Objects with a large mass also weigh more. To work out the weight of an object, we multiply its mass by 10.

A mass of 1 kilogram has a weight of 10 newtons. We can also write this as 10 N.

Mass multiplied by 10 = weight

1 multiplied by 10 = 10 newtons or 10 N

Be careful: to find weight in newtons you have to use the mass in kilograms, not grams.

Weight is a force; mass is the amount of 'stuff'.

ⓓ **A pet rabbit has a mass of 15 kilograms. What is its weight in newtons?**

KEY POINTS

- Weight is a force.

- Friction is a force.

- We measure forces in newtons (N).

- We measure mass in kilograms (kg).

- We can convert mass into newtons by multiplying by 10.

QUESTIONS

1 True or false? Copy out each sentence and put a tick or a cross next to it.

a Force is measured in newtons.

b Mass is measured in newtons.

c You can find the weight of an object by multiplying its mass by 10.

Why do some things float?

Some things float.
Some things sink.

ⓐ Make a list of five different things that float.

Polystyrene floats in water.

If you try to push it down under the water you can feel it pushing back against your hand. We call this force **upthrust**.

If you let go of the polystyrene under water, the upthrust pushes it back to the surface.

How do we measure upthrust?

We can measure upthrust using a force meter. You hang an object from a force meter and write down its weight. Then you hang the object in a beaker of water and write down its weight again. Remember: you measure weight in newtons (N).

Look at the pictures below. You will see that the object weighs less in water than it does in air. This difference in weight is the upthrust.

ⓑ If an object weighs 5.5 N in air and 3.5 N in water, what is the force of the upthrust?

Will it sink, or will it float?

If the upthrust on an object is equal to its weight the object will float.

If the weight of the object is greater than the upthrust, the object will sink.

ⓒ What is the name of the force that keeps you afloat when you are swimming?

You can have two objects with the same weight, but one floats and one sinks. Why?

Look at the picture. The brass rod, the water and the wood each have the same weight. But the brass rod will sink and the wood will float.

ⓓ What other difference can you see between the brass rod and the wood?

You may have noticed that the brass rod is much smaller than the wood, even though they weigh the same. We say that the brass has a higher **density** than the wood. This is why brass sinks and wood floats.

Water also has density. Things that are more dense than water will sink. Things that are less dense than water will float.

QUESTIONS

Copy these sentences and fill in the spaces using the words below:

        float   sink   upthrust

The force that stops an object sinking is called _____ . If an objects weighs more than the upthrust it will _____ . If an object is less dense than water it will _____ .

KEY POINTS

- Things weigh less in water because of upthrust.

- If the upthrust on an object is equal to its weight, it will float.

- Objects float if their density is less than the density of water.

Why do ships float?

Ships are very heavy. But they float. This is because the ships are very, very big. This makes them less dense than water.

If a ship was crushed up into a ball of metal, it would still weigh the same. But it would be much smaller. This would make it very dense. It would be denser than water and it would not float.

ⓐ **Why would a ship not float if it was crushed up into a ball of metal?**

Upthrust in air

Upthrust also works in air. The upthrust is so small that we do not usually notice it. But if we make a light object very big, it will even float in air.

If we fill an airship with helium, it is so light that it will float in the air.

Hot air is less dense than cold air. This is why hot air rises. A hot air balloon floats in air.

ⓑ **Why do hot gas and smoke from a fire go up a chimney?**

Archimedes

A Greek scientist thought about density and why things float. His name was Archimedes and he lived over 2000 years ago.

The King gave Archimedes a problem. Someone had made some gold jewellery for him. But he was suspicious that the jewellers had not used pure gold. He thought that they were trying to cheat him.

He asked Archimedes to find out if the jewellery was made of pure gold. Archimedes thought very hard how to solve the problem.

One day when he was having a bath, an idea came to him. He was so excited that he shouted out 'Eureka!'. This is Greek for 'I know the answer'.

Archimedes already knew that real gold would have a different density from fake gold. But he had just discovered a way to work out the density of real gold. When he had worked out the two densities, the density of the King's gold was different from the density of the real gold. He knew that the jewellers had tried to cheat the King.

C **How did Archimedes know the jewellers had tried to cheat the King?**

QUESTIONS

Copy these sentences and fill in the spaces using the words below:

> Archimedes   float   upthrust

Airships _____ in air. This is because air has _____ . A famous scientist called _____ used ideas about density to find out whether the King's gold was real or fake.

KEY POINTS

- Upthrust also happens in air.
- Archimedes was a Greek scientist who used the idea of density.

HOW DO FORCES BALANCE?

What happens when forces are balanced?

Forces are balanced when they cancel each other out.

Look at the picture of the tug-of-war. Both teams are pulling as hard as they can. But both teams are pulling the same amount so the rope does not move. The forces are balanced.

Look at the picture of the cat. Although it is not so obvious, the forces are also balanced here.

The cat has weight. But the table stops the cat from falling. It is pushing the cat upwards with the same force as the cat's weight pushing downwards. The forces are balanced.

Forces can even be balanced when things move

If an object is moving at a constant speed, the forces are balanced. If they were not balanced, the object would be speeding up or slowing down.

What happens when forces are not balanced?

When forces are not balanced, one of the following three things always happens.

- An object speeds up.
- An object slows down.
- An object changes direction.

Look at the pictures.

A girl on a bike.
She is speeding up.

A bunjee jumper.
He is slowing down.

A sprinter. The starting
gun has not yet been fired.

ⓐ In which of the three pictures are the forces balanced?

How do we show forces in diagrams?

We can show forces in diagrams by using arrows.
The bigger the arrow, the bigger the force.

Look at the picture. The woman is holding the dumbbell still. Her effort and the weight of the dumbbell are balanced. This is why both arrows are drawn the same size.

ⓑ If the woman lifted the dumbbell, which arrow would be bigger?

Effort

Weight

KEY POINTS

● Things speed up, slow down or change direction when forces are not balanced.

● We can use arrows to show forces in a diagram.

QUESTIONS

Write down two examples where forces are not balanced.

FORCES AND THEIR EFFECTS

What is friction?

Friction is a force. It tries to stop things from moving. It is usually caused when two surfaces rub together.

We can make friction less by making the surfaces smoother. We can also make friction less by using **lubrication**. A lubricant such as oil keeps rough surfaces apart, so they slide over each other more easily.

Oiling your bicycle chain will help to reduce friction.

How is friction useful?

Without friction life would be very difficult. A car uses friction to move forward.

If there was no friction between the tyre and the road, the wheels would spin but the car would stay still.

When it is icy, there is much less friction between the tyres and the road. The tyres can spin when it is icy, making driving difficult.

movement

push of tyre · friction between tyre and road

How do we measure speed?

In the UK, we measure speed in miles per hour. In other places people use kilometres per hour. In science we use metres per second.

These units may sound different but they are all just a measure of how fast something is moving. They tell us how far something has moved in a certain time.

We calculate **speed** by dividing the distance moved by the time taken.

$$\text{speed} = \frac{\text{distance}}{\text{time}}$$

If a sledge moves 20 metres in 2 seconds, how fast is it travelling? To find out, we divide 20 by 2.

$$\text{speed} = \frac{20}{2}$$

This tells us that it moved 10 metres in one second. We write this as 10 m/s.

ⓐ **If Joel runs 100 metres in 20 seconds, how fast is he running? (Remember: speed = the distance divided by the time.)**

Using graphs to show speed

The graph shows the journey of a bus.

ⓑ **How long was the bus journey?**

ⓒ **How far had the bus travelled after 5 hours?**

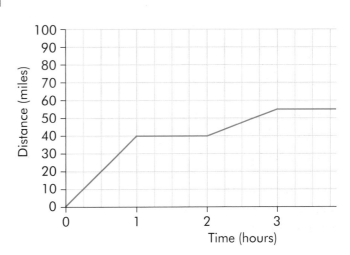

QUESTIONS

Copy these sentences and fill in the spaces using the words below:

> friction   time   lubricant

_____ is a force caused when two surfaces rub together. We can reduce friction by using a _____ . We calculate speed by dividing distance by _____ .

KEY POINTS

- Friction is a force that resists things moving.

- Speed equals distance divided by time.

How much does a spring stretch?

All things stretch when you pull them, but some things stretch more than others. Springs are meant to stretch when you pull them, and then go back to the length they were before.

Some students carried out an experiment to see how far a spring would stretch. They hung different masses from a spring. They measured how far the spring stretched. We call this stretching distance the **extension**.

Look at the table. It shows how big the extension was when the students hung different masses from the spring.

Mass hung on spring (g)	Extension (mm)
0	0
20	7
40	15
60	22
80	28
100	34
120	41
140	50
160	57
180	62
200	72
220	80
240	90
260	95

Use the results in the table to plot a graph. Copy the axes here to help you.

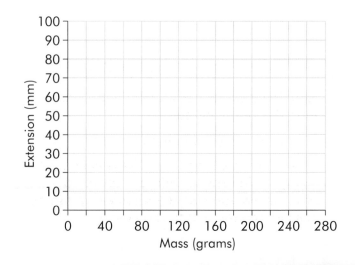

Investigating friction

To investigate friction, you attach a force meter to a block of wood. Place a mass on top of the wood. Gently pull the force meter until the wooden block starts to move.

Write down the reading on the force meter when the block starts to move.

This reading tells you how much force you needed to pull with, to overcome the force of friction.

What would happen to the force of friction if you:

a used the same block and mass but did it in a tray of sand?

b used the same block and mass but did it on a sheet of ice?

c used a bigger block?

d put a bigger mass on the block?

QUESTIONS

Copy these sentences and fill in the spaces using the words below:

extension   force meter   original

The amount a spring stretches is called the _____ . The spring will go back to its _____ length when you take the force away. We can measure the force of friction using a _____ .

KEY POINTS

- All things stretch when you pull them, but some things stretch more than others.

- Springs stretch when you pull them, but can go back to their original length.

- We can measure the force of friction with a force meter.

L1 WHERE AND WHAT IS THE EARTH?

What is the Earth?

When we look at the Earth from space it is the shape of a ball.

But when we look at it from ground level, it looks flat. This is because the Earth is so big you cannot see its curve when you are standing on it.

a Look at the pictures. Why did people used to think the Earth was flat?

How does the Earth spin?

The Earth is like an apple spinning on a rod pushed through its centre. The rod is held at an angle.

The Earth does not have a real rod through its centre. It is an imaginary one that goes from the **North Pole** to the **South Pole**.

The imaginary rod is called the Earth's **axis**.

b What is the Earth's axis?

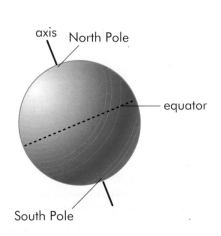

Why is there day and night?

During the day, your bit of the Earth is facing the Sun. At night, the Earth has spun round so that your bit is no longer facing the Sun.

The Earth takes 24 hours to spin round once. This is why one day and one night last for 24 hours.

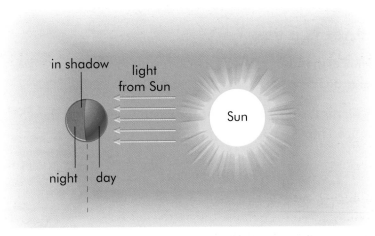

Why does the Sun seem to move across the sky?

Look at the picture. It shows the Earth turning as we see it from above.

Imagine you are standing on the red dot. You start at sunrise. As the Earth turns the Sun appears to move. Soon it will be noon. Later it will be sunset.

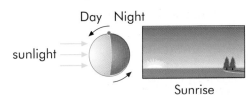

Sunrise

Time around the world

Because the Earth is turning on its axis, it is a different time in different places. When it is noon on one side of the Earth, it will be midnight on the other side.

Some countries such as America are so big that it is a different time on different sides of the country.

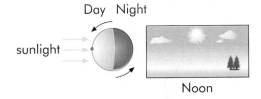

Noon

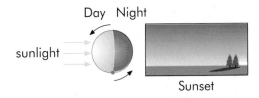

Sunset

QUESTIONS

1 How many times will the Earth spin in one week?

2 How much of the Earth is lit by the Sun at any one time?

3 The Earth spins a little slower each year. What will this do to the length of a day?

KEY POINTS

- The Earth is a large round ball floating in space.

- The Earth spins on its axis. This causes day and night.

WHAT CAUSES THE YEAR AND THE SEASONS?

What is a year?

The Earth moves in a large circle round the Sun. It takes 365 days for the Earth to go round the Sun once.

A year is the time it takes for the Earth to go round the Sun. So there are 365 days in a year.

Why are there seasons?

In the UK we have seasons.

Summer is warm with long days and short nights.

Winter is cold with short days and long nights.

Spring and autumn are in between.

We have seasons because the Earth is tilted.

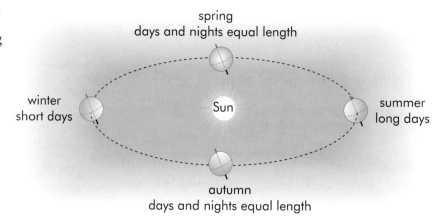

Look at picture **A** below. The shadow shows the half of the Earth that is in night. The other half is in day.

In the summer the UK is tilted towards the Sun. Look at the dotted line. The part in daylight is much longer than the part in the shadow. This means that in summer, the days are long and the nights are short.

In the winter the UK is tilted away from the Sun. Look at picture **B**. You can see that the days are much shorter than the nights.

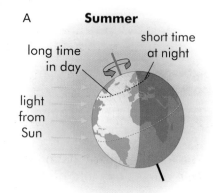

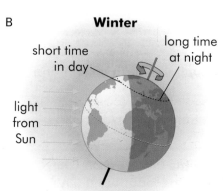

When the top half of the Earth is tilted toward the Sun, the bottom half is tilted away from the Sun.

ⓐ **Australia is on the opposite side of the Earth to the UK. Why do they have summer when we have winter?**

Why is the Sun high in the sky in summer?

Look at the picture below. In the UK the Sun is high in the sky in summer, and low in the sky in winter.

The Sun is high in the sky in summer because the Earth is tilted towards the Sun.

ⓑ **Why is the Sun low in the sky in winter?**

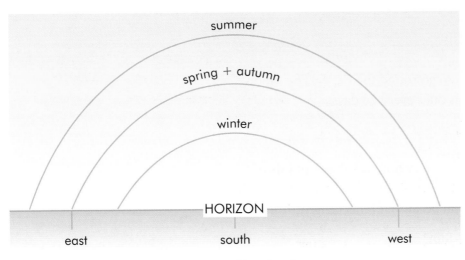

The Sun is high in the sky in summer, and low in winter.

QUESTIONS

Copy these sentences and fill in the spaces using the words below:

     higher   seasons   Sun   year

It takes one _____ for the Earth to go round the _____ . We have _____ because the Earth is tilted. This also makes the Sun rise _____ in the sky in summer.

KEY POINTS

● A year is the time it takes for the Earth to go round the Sun.

● We have summer and winter because the Earth is tilted.

● In the summer we are tilted towards the Sun. In the winter we are tilted away from the Sun.

The Moon

Just as the Earth goes round the Sun, the Moon is a smaller ball of rock going round the Earth.

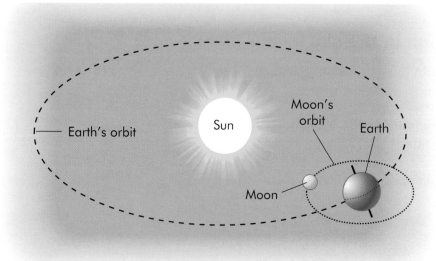

The Moon takes 28 days to go round the Earth. The Moon also spins on its own axis once every 28 days.

How do we see the Sun and the Moon?

We see the Sun because it is very hot and gives out lots of light. The Moon is cold and does not give out any light at all. We can only see the Moon because it reflects light from the Sun.

ⓐ **Why can we see the Sun?**

ⓑ **Why can we see the Moon?**

What is an eclipse?

In an **eclipse**, we see a shadow in front of the Moon or the Sun. There are two kinds of eclipse.

Solar eclipse

A **solar eclipse** happens when the Moon passes in front of the Sun. The Sun goes dark for a while.

Although the Moon is much smaller than the Sun, it is much closer to us. By pure chance they both look the same size. So when they line up, the Moon completely covers the Sun for a couple of minutes.

Lunar eclipse

In a **lunar eclipse**, the Moon goes dark for a while.

This happens when the Moon passes behind the Earth, where the Sun cannot reach it. The Moon goes into shadow. The shadow is cast by the Earth.

The Moon can no longer reflect the light from the Sun. Because the Earth is bigger than the Moon, the Earth casts a big shadow. This is why lunar eclipses can last for two hours.

C Which lasts longer, a solar eclipse or a lunar eclipse?

QUESTIONS

Copy these sentences and fill in the spaces using the words below. You can use each word more than once.

Earth   Moon   Sun

The _____ goes round the Earth every 28 days. It reflects light from the _____ . When the _____ goes between the Earth and the Sun there is a solar eclipse. A lunar eclipse happens when the Moon goes into the shadow of the _____ .

KEY POINTS

- The Moon goes round the Earth every 28 days.

- The Sun is hot and gives off light.

- The Moon is cold and reflects light from the Sun.

- A solar eclipse happens when the Moon goes between the Earth and the Sun.

- A lunar eclipse happens when the Moon passes into the Earth's shadow.

WHAT DOES THE SOLAR SYSTEM CONSIST OF?

What is the solar system?

The **solar system** has nine large balls of material called **planets**.

They all go round the Sun.

Just like the Earth, some of the planets have moons.

How big is the Sun?

The Sun is very large. It is 110 times bigger than the Earth.

How big are the planets?

Look at the picture. Look for the Earth and see which planets are bigger and which are smaller.

ⓐ **Which is the biggest planet?**

ⓑ **Which is the smallest planet?**

ⓒ **Which planets are about the same size as the Earth?**

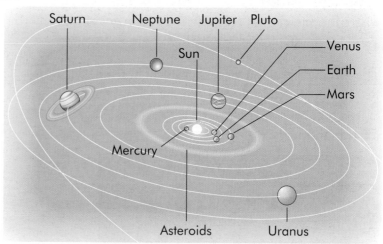

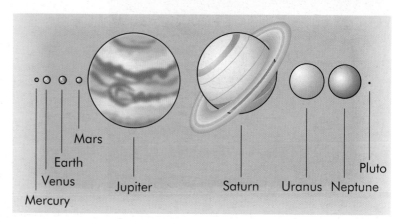

How far is the Earth away from the Sun?

Imagine standing at one end of a swimming pool holding a grain of sugar. If the grain of sugar was the Earth, the Sun would be the size of a grapefruit at the other end of the swimming pool.

Pluto would be the size of a piece of dust over 1 km away.

QUESTIONS

Look at the picture opposite and answer the following questions.

1 How many moons has Jupiter?

2 How far is Pluto from the Sun?

3 Is Mars closer to the Sun than Earth is, or further away?

KEY POINTS

● The solar system consists of nine planets going round the Sun.

● The distances between the planets and the Sun are very large.

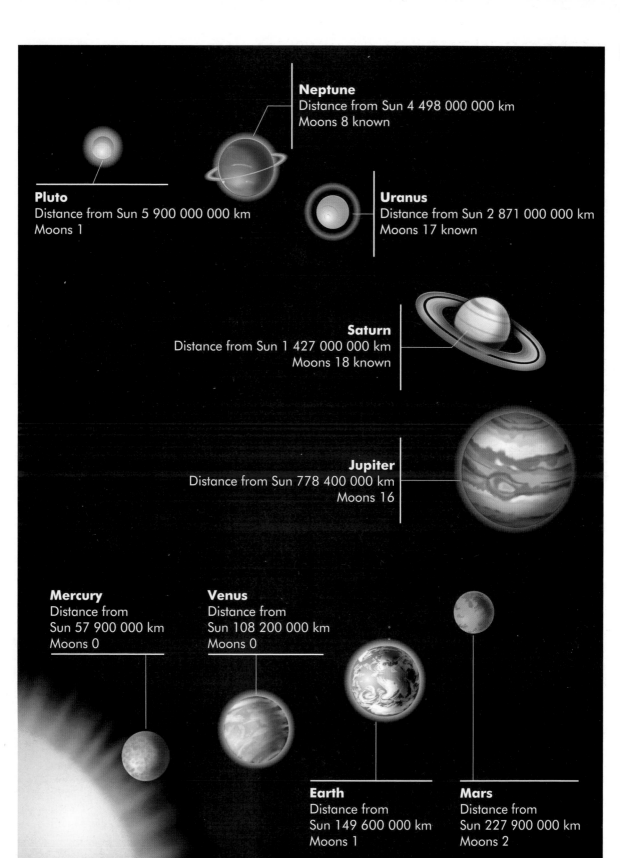

Neptune
Distance from Sun 4 498 000 000 km
Moons 8 known

Pluto
Distance from Sun 5 900 000 000 km
Moons 1

Uranus
Distance from Sun 2 871 000 000 km
Moons 17 known

Saturn
Distance from Sun 1 427 000 000 km
Moons 18 known

Jupiter
Distance from Sun 778 400 000 km
Moons 16

Mercury
Distance from
Sun 57 900 000 km
Moons 0

Venus
Distance from
Sun 108 200 000 km
Moons 0

Earth
Distance from
Sun 149 600 000 km
Moons 1

Mars
Distance from
Sun 227 900 000 km
Moons 2

Where are the stars?

The Sun is a star. It looks bigger than the other stars because it is much closer to the Earth. All the other stars are a very long way from the Earth.

We can imagine how far stars are away by thinking about how fast light travels.

Light years

Light will travel from the UK to America in a fraction of a second. But it takes $8\frac{1}{2}$ minutes for light to travel from the Sun to the Earth.

Light will travel from the next nearest star to the Earth in $4\frac{1}{2}$ years. But light from some stars takes millions of years to reach the Earth.

These stars are so far away that they just look like pinpoints of light. They are so far away that scientists have to use a new form of measurement.

This measurement is the distance that light travels in one year. Light travels 9 461 000 000 000 km in one year. This distance is called a **light year**.

ⓐ **Why do scientists measure the distance to the stars using a unit called a 'light year'?**

Why can't we see stars during the day?

Stars are very faint because they are so far away.

The Sun is very bright. It is so bright that we can only see the stars at night, when we cannot see the light from the Sun.

How do we use the stars?

The stars always have the same pattern in the sky. This can be useful when we want to find our way.

One of the stars is called the Pole Star. This is because it is always above the North Pole. If you know how to find the Pole Star in the sky, you will never get lost. This is because you will always know which direction north is.

Look at the picture. It shows you how to find the Pole Star.

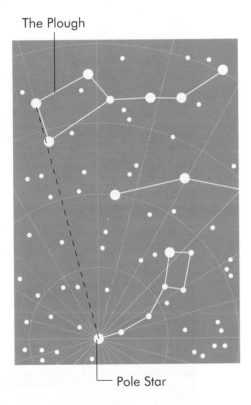

The Plough

Pole Star

QUESTIONS

Copy these sentences and fill in the spaces using the words below. You can use each word more than once.

Pole   Sun

The closest star to the Earth is called the _____ . The _____ Star is always above the North Pole. It is much further away than the _____ .

IS THERE LIFE ANYWHERE ELSE?

What sort of planet can support life?

We know that the Earth has life on it. But does life exist on any other planet?

Life on Earth needs three things to survive:

1 liquid water
2 sunlight
3 carbon.

Earth has plenty of these three things. For life to exist on any other planet it may also need to have water, sunlight and carbon.

Remember: if water is too hot it turns to steam. If it is too cold it turns to ice. Water turns into steam at 100 °C and into ice at 0 °C.

Look at the picture of the planets to see which one of them is just right to have liquid water.

ⓐ Which planet has liquid water and could support life?

ⓑ What is the temperature on Pluto?

ⓒ What is the temperature on Mars?

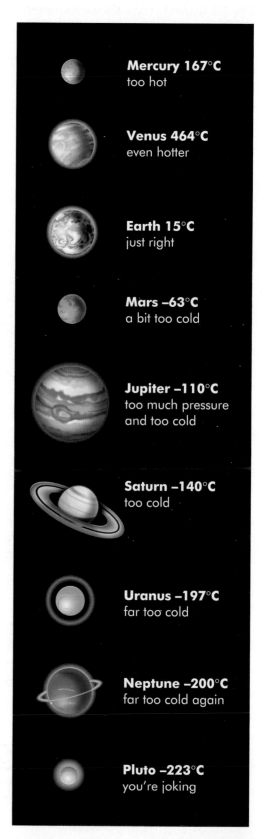

Mercury 167°C
too hot

Venus 464°C
even hotter

Earth 15°C
just right

Mars –63°C
a bit too cold

Jupiter –110°C
too much pressure and too cold

Saturn –140°C
too cold

Uranus –197°C
far too cold

Neptune –200°C
far too cold again

Pluto –223°C
you're joking

Was there life on Mars?

Mars is now so cold that the water there is frozen. But millions of years ago Mars may have been warmer. The water may have been liquid and there may have been life.

Looking for life

Mars is so far away that it is difficult to tell if there was ever life there.

Scientists have sent spacecraft called Viking landers to land on Mars and look for signs of life. Scientists are planning to send people to Mars in the near future.

Are there planets out there like Earth?

We don't know. But scientists are finding planets that are going round stars hundreds of light years away.

There are an awful lot of stars and some of them may have planets just like the Earth. Until we make contact with aliens, we may never know.

QUESTIONS

Copy these sentences and fill in the spaces using the words below:

cold   Mars   water

Planets need _____ , light and carbon to support life. Other planets in the solar system are too hot or too _____ to have liquid water. _____ may once have supported life.

KEY POINTS

- Planets need water, light and carbon to support life.

- Mars may once have supported life.

WHAT IS BEYOND THE SOLAR SYSTEM?

Looking at the sky

For thousands of years people have looked at the stars in the sky. Using just your **naked eye** you can see thousands of stars. You can even see most of the planets in the solar system.

Telescopes

In the year 1610, a man called Galileo used one of the first **telescopes**. A telescope helps you see distant things more clearly.

The top picture is a modern photograph of the planet Saturn that Galileo saw using his early telescope.

ⓐ What do you notice that is unusual about the planet?

Galileo also found four moons round Saturn. He discovered that there were more stars than anybody had realised.

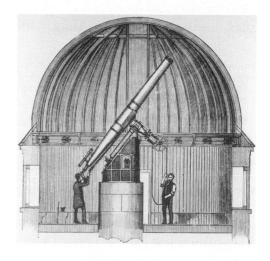

The first telescopes were kept in buildings called observatories. This picture shows an observatory.

A telescope in space

Scientists now have much bigger telescopes.

The Hubble space telescope is in space, travelling around the Earth. Because there is no air in the way, it gives much better pictures than telescopes on Earth.

ⓑ Why does the Hubble space telescope give much better pictures?

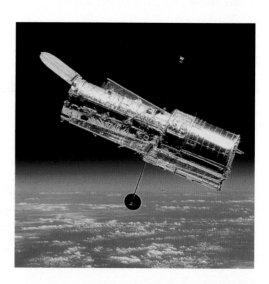

Space exploration

Because the stars are so far away, we have not been able to send spacecraft to them. But the planets in the solar system are closer. Scientists have sent spacecraft to look at most of them.

The Moon is even closer. It is so close that people have gone to the Moon and landed safely on it.

KEY POINTS

- For thousands of years people looked at the sky with just their naked eye.

- For the last few hundred years, scientists have used telescopes to look at the sky.

- Modern telescopes are very powerful. They give us information about the planets and the stars.

- The Moon is our closest neighbour. People have visited the Moon.

QUESTIONS

Copy these sentences and fill in the spaces using the words below:

> Galileo   Moon   stars   telescope

A man called _____ was one of the first people to use a _____ . Scientists discovered that the _____ was so close that we could send people to visit it. _____ are much further away, too far to visit in a spacecraft.

Glossary

acid   substance that reacts with **alkalis** and may have a sour taste

adapted   when plants, animals or **cells** have special features which help them to survive or do their job

adolescence   part of life between childhood and adulthood during which **puberty** happens

afterbirth   name for the **placenta** when it passes out of the woman's body after **birth**

alkali   substance that reacts with **acids**

ammeter   device for measuring electric **current**

amniotic fluid   fluid surrounding and protecting the baby in the **uterus**

amp   unit of electric **current**

antacid   substance that uses up or cancels out an **acid**

atom   the smallest bit of something

axis   imaginary line the Earth rotates around

bacteria   tiny living things that can cause disease

battery   two or more **cells** working one after the other

bicarbonate of soda   another name for sodium hydrogen carbonate

birth   when the baby is pushed out of a woman's **uterus**

bone   **tissue** that is rigid and supports you

bud   part of a plant that makes new **leaves** or **flowers**

carbon dioxide   colourless gas that turns **limewater** milky

carbonate   chemical that reacts with an **acid** and gives off **carbon dioxide**

carnivore   animal which eats only other animals

cell (Unit A)   building block of animals and plants

cell (Unit J)   part in an electrical **circuit** that pushes the **current** around

cell membrane   holds the **cytoplasm** together and controls what goes into and out of the **cell**

cell wall   stops the **cell** changing shape, collapsing or bursting

chemical change   change which makes a new substance or substances

chemical reaction   another name for **chemical change**

chloroplast   place in the cells where plants make food

choice chamber   apparatus that allows animals to choose between two different places

chromatogram	'colour picture' you get as the result of **chromatography**	**density**	how heavy a certain volume of substance is
chromatography	method of separating a **mixture** of **solutes**	**develop**	change physically and emotionally
circuit diagram	**symbols** representing an electrical **circuit**	**diffusion**	spreading out movement of **particles**
circuit	complete route from the positive end of a **cell** or **battery** to the negative end	**distillation**	separating and collecting the **solvent** from a **mixture**
classifying	putting things into groups	**dormant**	protected to survive harsh conditions
condense	change from a gas to a liquid	**eclipse**	when there is a shadow in front of the Moon or the Sun
conductors	materials that allow heat or electricity to move through them easily	**egg cell**	female **cell** for reproduction in humans and plants
consumers	animals, which must eat other living things for food	**electric current**	flow of **electrons** round a **circuit**
contract, contractions	what the **uterus** muscles do when they push the baby out during **birth**	**electrons**	charged particles that can move through **conductors**
corrode	to eat away a substance	**embryo**	bundle of **cells** resulting from **fertilisation**, before separate **organs develop**
corrosive	can **corrode** something. A corrosive substance attacks and destroys living **tissue**, including eyes and skin	**energy**	ability to make things happen
		environment	surroundings in a **habitat**
cover slip	place this over your sample when you look at it under the **microscope**	**environmental factors**	conditions in a **habitat** which affect what can live there
current	flow of **electrons** round a **circuit**	**environmental variation**	features which have been affected by surroundings
cytoplasm	place where **chemical reactions** happen in a **cell**	**evaporate**	change from a liquid to a gas

extension	how much longer a material becomes when stretched	**gas**	form of matter that changes its shape and its size
external fertilisation	when **fertilisation** happens outside the female's body	**gel**	**mixture** of a **liquid** and a **solid**
fertilisation	when the male and female **cells** join together in reproduction	**geothermal**	**energy** transferred from heat inside the Earth
filtering	method of separating **solid** bits from a **liquid**	**gestation period**	time during which a woman is **pregnant**
fire triangle	picture used to show the three things a fire needs to burn	**gills**	a fish gets **oxygen** from the water through these
flower	part of a plant that makes seeds for reproduction	**grow, growth**	increase in size
foam	**mixture** of a **gas** and a **liquid** *or* a **gas** and a **solid**	**habitat**	place where an animal or plant lives
focusing knobs	you turn these to focus a microscope	**harmful**	can make you ill if swallowed, breathed in or absorbed through the skin
food chain	picture showing what an animal eats and what eats it	**hazard symbol**	symbol used to warn about substances that are **corrosive**, **harmful** or **irritant**
food web	picture made of lots of joined up **food chains,** showing what eats what in a **habitat**	**herbivore**	animal which eats only plants
force	a push or a pull, which can move something or stop something moving	**hibernation**	when an animal spends the winter asleep
fossil fuel	**fuel** made from the bodies of animals or plants that lived millions of years ago (coal, oil, gas)	**hydroelectricity**	transforming the **energy** from moving water into electrical energy
friction	**force** acting against movement when two surfaces touch	**hydrogen**	colourless gas that 'pops' with a lighted splint
fuel	substance that we can burn to release heat **energy**	**identical twins**	twins who look exactly the same, formed from the same **fertilised egg cell**
fuse	safety device that stops **current** flowing if the current gets too high	**implantation**	the **embryo** attaches itself to the **uterus** lining
		impurities	unwanted substances mixed with the substance you want

incubator	apparatus that keeps the temperature the same for organisms to live in	**limewater**	another name for calcium hydroxide solution, used to test for **carbon dioxide**
indicator	chemical that changes colour in **acids** and **alkalis**	**liquid**	form of matter that keeps its size but changes its shape
inherit	pass on from one generation to the next	**lubrication**	putting a substance such as oil between two surfaces to reduce **friction**
inherited variation	those of your features which were passed on to you by your parents	**lunar eclipse**	when the Moon moves through the Earth's shadow
insoluble	a substance that won't dissolve in a **solvent** is insoluble	**magnification**	how much bigger an image is than the object
insulators	materials that do not allow heat or electricity to pass through them easily	**mass**	how much 'stuff' an object has
internal fertilisation	when **fertilisation** happens inside the female's body	**menstrual cycle**	monthly cycle of changes in the female **reproductive organs**
invertebrate	animal without a backbone	**menstruation**	monthly loss of the **uterus** lining from a woman's body through the **vagina**
irritant	may cause reddening or blistering of the skin		
joule	unit of **energy**	**methane**	gas that burns easily and is used as a fuel, made from **hydrogen** and carbon
kilogram	unit of **mass**		
kingdom	living things can be divided into five kingdoms e.g. the animal kingdom and the plant kingdom	**microscope**	used to look at very small things
labour	time leading up to **birth** when the **uterus** muscles are **contracting**	**migration**	movement of animals across long distances in search of food
leaf	part of a plant that makes food	**mirror**	reflects light up through the **microscope**
lenses	parts of a **microscope** that magnify the **specimen**	**mixture**	two or more substances that are mixed together
light year	distance light travels in one year, unit used to measure distances of stars	**model**	way of imagining how something works

muscle	**tissue** that pulls on **bone** so you can move
naked eye	looking at objects without a **microscope**, **telescope** or binoculars
nerve cell	**cell** that carries messages around the human body
neutral	neither **acidic** nor **alkaline**
newton	unit of **force**
non-identical twins	twins who do not look exactly the same, formed two different **fertilised egg cells**
non-renewable energy resource	energy resource that is not replaced after it is used
North Pole	point at the northern end of the Earth's **axis**
nucleus	controls what happens inside a **cell**
nutrition	process of making, getting and using food
organ	structure in a plant or animal which has a special job and is made up of **tissues**
ovaries	**organs** that make **egg cells** in humans and plants
oviduct	tube connecting an **ovary** with the **uterus** in women
ovulation	release of an **egg cell** from an **ovary** into the **oviduct**
oxide	substance containing **oxygen** joined to something else
oxygen	colourless gas that relights a glowing splint
parallel circuit	electrical **circuit** with more than one path for the **current** to flow
particles	tiny bits of something
penis	places **sperm** inside a female's **vagina** during **sexual intercourse**
period	see **menstruation**
pH scale	range of strengths of **acids** and **alkalis**, from 0 to 14
placenta	**organ** through which the baby gets food and **oxygen** and gets rid of waste during **pregnancy**
planets	large spheres moving round the Sun
pollen cell	male **cell** for reproduction in plants
pollination	moving a pollen grain to the **stigma** of a flower
predator	animal which hunts other animals for food
pregnant	a woman is **pregnant** when a baby is growing and **developing** inside her
premature	when a baby is born early, before it is fully grown and **developed**
pressure	**gas** pushing on the sides of its container
prey	animal which is hunted and eaten by another animal
producers	plants which make their own food using **energy** from the Sun

puberty	time during **adolescence** when your body **develops** sexually	**skin**	**tissue** that holds everything together
red blood cell	**cell** that carries **oxygen** around the body	**solar eclipse**	when the Moon passes in front of the Sun and the Sun goes dark
renewable energy resource	source of energy that is continually replaced	**solar energy**	energy from the Sun
reproductive organs	the **organs** used to make a new living thing	**solar panel**	collects **solar energy** as heat
		solar system	the Sun and nine **planets** that move round it
resistance	how difficult it is for electric **current** to flow	**solid**	form of matter that keeps the same shape and size
ring main	electrical **circuit** used in houses for power	**solubility**	how much **solute** dissolves in a **solvent**
rock salt	mixture of salt and rock that is found underground	②**soluble**	a substance that will dissolve in a **solvent** is soluble
root	part of a plant that takes in water and holds the plant firm in the soil	③**solute**	substance that has dissolved in a **solvent**
root hair cell	**cell** that absorbs water from the soil for a plant	①**solution**	mixture of a **solvent** and one or more **solutes**
saturated solution	**solution** in which no more **solute** can dissolve	**solvent**	**liquid** that something will dissolve in
scrotum	bag of skin that holds the **testes**	**South Pole**	point at the southern end of the Earth's **axis**
sea salt	salt left when the water is **evaporated** from sea water	**species**	living things which have almost all of their features in common
sexual intercourse	when a man puts **sperm** into a woman's **vagina** using his **penis**	**specimen**	the sample that you look at under a **microscope**
short circuit	path around a part in a **circuit**, with very little **resistance**	**speed**	how far something moves in a certain time
simple circuit	electrical **circuit** with only one possible path	**sperm cell**	male **cell** for reproduction in humans

sperm duct	tube that carries **sperm** from the **testes** to the **penis**	**upthrust**	**force** of water or other liquid/gas pushing an object upwards
stage	part of a **microscope** where you put the **specimen**	**uterus**	**organ** in which a baby **develops** inside its mother
stage clips	hold the slide on the **stage** of a **microscope**	**vacuole**	contains the cell sap (a store of water, salt and sugar)
stem	part of a plant that holds up the **leaves** and **flowers**	**vagina**	place inside the woman where **sperm** are placed during **sexual intercourse**
stigma	part of a flower where pollen grains must land for **pollination** to happen	**variation**	the way in which living things look different from each other
streamlined	thin and pointed shape which moves easily through air or water	**vertebrate**	animal with a backbone
		volt	unit of electrical push
symbol	sign that means something	**waters breaking**	when the **amniotic fluid** passes out of the mother before **birth**
telescope	used to look at stars and planets that are a long way away	**weight**	**force** that pulls a **mass** downwards
temperature	how hot or cold something is		
tendon	**tissue** that joins a **muscle** to a **bone**	**xylem**	**tissue** found in plant stems that carries water
testes	place where **sperm** are made in humans		
theory	idea		
thermometer	used for measuring **temperature**		
tissue	group of similar **cells** which work together to do the same job		
umbilical cord	this connects the **developing** baby to the **placenta** inside the **uterus**		
Universal Indicator	mixture of dyes that shows the strength of an **acid** or **alkali**		